PENGUI

BUSTER'S FIR

Geoff Burrell was born in Lei University of Sheffield, where ~~he obtained~~ in Psychology and a Postgraduate Diploma in Business Studies. He has done a variety of jobs, including working as a gardener, shop assistant and labourer. In 1985 he qualified as a Registered Mental Nurse and has worked as a staff nurse and as a charge nurse on wards for the Elderly Severely Mentally Infirm. Geoff Burrell is married and lives in Lincolnshire.

GEOFF BURRELL

Buster's Fired a Wobbler
A Week in a Psychiatric Hospital

PENGUIN BOOKS

PENGUIN BOOKS

Published by the Penguin Group
27 Wrights Lane, London W8 5TZ, England
Viking Penguin Inc., 40 West 23rd Street, New York, New York 10010, USA
Penguin Books Australia Ltd, Ringwood, Victoria, Australia
Penguin Books Canada Ltd, 2801 John Street, Markham, Ontario, Canada L3R 1B4
Penguin Books (NZ) Ltd, 182–190 Wairau Road, Auckland 10, New Zealand

Penguin Books Ltd, Registered Offices: Harmondsworth, Middlesex, England

First published 1989
10 9 8 7 6 5 4 3 2 1

Copyright © Geoff Burrell, 1989
All rights reserved

Filmset in 10/12 Linotron Plantin
by Centracet

Made and printed in Great Britain by
Cox & Wyman, Reading

Except in the United States of America, this book is sold
subject to the condition that it shall not, by way of trade or otherwise,
be lent, re-sold, hired out, or otherwise circulated without the publisher's
prior consent in any form of binding or cover other than that in which it is
published and without a similar condition including this condition
being imposed on the subsequent purchaser

Author's Note

The events described in this book took place over several years during which I nursed in or visited a number of different NHS hospitals catering for the mentally ill. These experiences are here compressed into a short period, using fictional characters and descriptive detail throughout.

For Maggie

Introduction

It would take 55 minutes' hard walking on a good day to get there from town. Uphill all the way but not too steep. At first there are houses, then factories, along the road, but pretty soon they thin out and eventually drop behind until there is nothing left but the country.

The hospital itself lies in a small pleat in the landscape, tucked out of sight of the motorway which skirts its western boundary. It can be seen from the minor road which takes the local village traffic, or you can get a closer look by boarding the single-decker bus from town that turns aside at the gates to enter this secluded place. A few people do pass through on foot but they invariably feel uncomfortable. In the distance are the cloud-shrouded hills and all around is undulation, a rumpled quilt of snow-smudged fields and hedges and roads.

From the bus the passengers look out over parkland where in summer cattle slowly graze between the scattered ancient oaks. Other features come into view across the winter landscape: a leafless orchard, a market garden, some desolate playing fields. Attention is temporarily diverted from the destination. Then a man starts to sing, the one who, though nobody could swear to this, looked as if he didn't have any socks on when he got on the bus in town. His foot starts to tap against the seat of the passenger in front, hard, repetitive, insistent.

As the bus slows, those on board see more. Here a tall boiler-house chimney, a sandstone church discoloured with green moss; there a car park, a man in a white coat, three nurses huddled in capes hurrying up the road, an ambulance parked, a man shouting. Unease has arrived and with it the buildings, suddenly close up and peopled. A main block of red brick piled three storeys high, brooded over by two formidable towers of differing designs and unknown use. The windows of the hospital look barred, but that is just imagination. They are merely glazed with small panes in thick frames. Two have closed shutters on the inside, but the significance of this is lost upon those passengers just passing through. Two three-storey buildings, close to the main block and extending forward from it, create a feeling of encirclement, as if the institution were reaching forward to close around the bus.

Out of sight of the bus, but close at hand, are small grassed courtyards and squares of larger lawns whose covering of snow is undisturbed by the excited tracks of children, strangers to this place. Beyond, more buildings are dotted around the park, most of them along the bus route. Some house medical staff, and in the largest one live the student nurses. Everywhere are tree-lined walks and shrubby borders. One leads to the mortuary. On what must be the cricket pitch the heavy roller lies waist deep in drifting snow. There is a fine pavilion, securely locked to keep out the patients, who on warm days sleep away their drugs in shady corners of the playing fields.

Outside the now stationary bus an obese man lies on a snow-covered park bench. He wears an old suit with an open-necked shirt, and smokes on a matchstick-sized roll-up. As each passenger disembarks he chuckles quietly to himself.

A visitor entering through the large wooden doors, brass fittings gleaming, is met inside by a smell that is junior school: boiled greens, waxed parquet, old flowers and carbolic soap. Ahead lies a spacious hall, with an antiquated switchboard behind the sign that says Enquiries. Half-tiled corridors tunnel deep into the institution. Along these pass smoking wraiths, bustling professionals, trundling trains of stainless-steel food trolleys. Labelled doors lead off into high-ceilinged rooms: Pharmacy, Administration, Nursing Officer, Kitchen. Further on a fine concert hall appears complete with stage and grand piano. Then the Bank, Café, Stores, Shop, Medical Records. And ward after ward after ward. All in a building constructed over a century ago, a home for Persons of Unsound Mind.

The wards are all slightly different but exactly the same. On each is found a dormitory, a day room, a dining room, a bathroom, usually with two baths, basic toilets. There is an office for the charge nurse, one for the psychiatrist, and a clinical room. Colours are smoke-browned pastels; ceilings are high; rooms are large and impersonal with chairs that are always placed with their backs against the walls, facing inwards. Some of these wards are training wards where students and pupils hope to learn their skills. Others are referred to as 'back wards'. Located in the bowels of the hospital, they are not considered suitable for training.

The Sisters or charge nurses run the wards. Beneath them are staff nurses and under them State Enrolled Nurses. Most wards also have a complement of auxiliary nurses. These are untrained staff who work under the direction of the trained nurses, or at least that's the theory. Then there are the student nurses, making up the numbers on the duty rota. And finally the pupil nurses, for whom all days are alike. Lacking prospects even when Enrolled, they really have the worst of all possible worlds.

The hospital has nearly 700 inmates. Some patients are described as being 'acute', or 'short-stay'. Many of these are also said to be 'on the roundabout', because of their frequent re-admissions. Long-stay patients are just that. Most staff know at least one patient with 60 years clocked up. Some patients are for 'rehabilitation', which means they are to be prepared for return to the community. Elderly people with 'mental infirmities' are also housed here, and there are places for day patients.

Among the patients a pecking order exists on each ward and across the hospital. The major determinant of status is possession of cigarettes, the most important drug used in the hospital, for which there is an insatiable demand. A capacity for violence will also earn a grudging respect from fellow patients and many staff. Sex is readily available if you are not too particular, enjoy the outdoor variety and have the cigarettes to pay for it. The patient's

3

day is hung around the domestic routine of the hospital. Breakfast. Dinner. Tea.

Over 200 people are required for the institution to function. These people are not without interest. A number of them suffer from the same maladies as their patients. Several members of the same family can usually be found working at the hospital at any one time, frequently spanning two, and occasionally three, generations, and some staff have relatives who are patients, though they are not allowed to care for them professionally. A few of today's patients were yesterday's staff.

Students and pupils are trained in theory at the School of Nursing. The school rightly insists that the pupils and students maintain certain standards. These are standards that the school does not teach and the hospital does not practise. This results in trainees suffering from burn-out. Often followed by drop-out. One in six of all trainees leave nursing before they finish their training, and six per cent qualify but never nurse. Such is the system.

One in ten of the UK population receive psychiatric treatment every year. Many of them will end up in a place just like the one reconstructed between the covers of this book. There isn't a psychiatric nurse in the country who won't recognize all or part of it. This, after all, is a normal psychiatric hospital. Normal that is, in the sense that it is the same as most of the others. Or, as a much-travelled staff nurse once said to me, 'Once you've seen inside one bin you've seen inside 'em all.'

Tuesday 18 December

'Do you want me to get his willy out?' asks Maisie, grabbing at my trousers. Fat Jack, our tutor, is not amused. 'Try and be serious for once, Student Nurse Campbell,' he snaps pompously. Which is a real joke coming from him, the biggest clown in the hospital. Maisie stops her one-handed attempts to undo my belt and I relax back on the hospital bed. Above me the Christmas decorations hung along the dormitory stir gently in the disturbed air. The rest of our group, convulsed with stifled laughter, stand around me. 'You want me to be serious!' Maisie expostulates, waving the long, green, worm-like catheter at Fat Jack, her stocky little Scottish frame filling with righteous indignation. 'You're supposed to be showing me how to catheterize somebody, all I've got to practise on is auld Buster here, and you want me to be serious! How on earth am I ever supposed to learn anything in this place?' Beneath her mass of ginger hair a roundish face questions the stupidity of this latest charade.

The snow has been cleared from the paths and roads by the patients who normally work on the gardens. I walk back to the School of Nursing with Joanna, another of the students in my group. We're still laughing over the indomitable Maisie. Joanna's a really nice girl. Divorced, but luckily without kids and young enough at 23 to make her way again. Which is what she's doing here. You can always spot the mature students. Suffering a few of life's knocks yourself is a wonderful window into the patient's world.

A figure approaches us, moving like a marionette. Yellow shoes, red trousers, orange shirt, green corduroy jacket, blue duffel-coat undone and flapping in the wind all add to the effect.

'Hello Tim,' greets Joanna in her sing-song North-country accent. Tim comes across to us. 'Aren't you cold?' Joanna says. Tim looks dazed, like a man recovering from a knock-out punch. Joanna starts to do up the toggles on his coat. Her skin glows with the bite of the wind. Tim's young face is emaciated and the mouth works constantly in silent conversation with his voices. He's had a shave but missed large patches of stubble on his neck. I give him a Polo mint and Joanna makes him put his hands in the pockets of his coat to keep them warm. It strikes me that the mass of curly hair is thinning drastically. Tim, who was first admitted here as an adolescent, will soon be going bald. 'Stop it, stop it, stop it,' he shouts in response to a voice only he can hear.

'Fancy letting him out looking like that!' Joanna reproaches, pushing the summer-straw hair away from where it blows across her eyes, speaking both our thoughts as Tim moves jerkily away down the road.

Joanna and I have returned via the hospital shop and the others are already having their coffee when we arrive. There are no decorations at the school. No sign of Christmas just around the corner. Maisie is in high spirits again. 'It's a good job I didnae have to really catheterize you, Buster,' she quips, 'I'd have never got a hold of that wee thing.' I grab her head. 'Who are you calling wee?' I joke, making as if to unzip my trousers. Maisie breaks away. 'Oh dinnae, dinnae,' she shouts. 'I'll be sick!'

There are six of us sitting round the coffee table, the only survivors of the larger group that started training three years previously. 'A week today,' states Rosemary, her voice a sugar-sweet melody from her native West Indies, 'and I'll be stuffing my face with Christmas goodies.' 'Since when did you need an excuse to stuff your face, you fat bitch?' hoots Maisie. 'Look who's talking,' Rosemary replies, laughing with the rest of us. 'Old egg on legs herself.' It's what passes for a normal conversation between these two, firm friends since the start of their training. In truth both of them are carrying slightly too much weight, the result of stodgy canteen food and the need to fill in boring off-duty hours in the hospital social club, isolated from the nearest town.

As we talk the door opens and a young charge nurse off one of the acute wards sticks his head into the room. 'Anybody seen Fat Jack?' he asks with a grin, using our tutor's universally applied nickname. 'I wouldn't tell you if I had,' snaps Rosemary, her voice losing its usual warmth. The head withdraws, no longer grinning. 'Take it easy,' I caution. 'It's best to keep in with these characters, you know.' Maisie chips in: 'Aye, but not if they grab a-hold of your tits and try and stick their hands up yer dress every time they catch you alone on the ward, eh Rosemary?' 'He's just a dirty pig,' Rosemary says with feeling. For a few minutes nobody speaks. 'I shan't be able to get home if this snow keeps up,' Joanna says quietly. 'Oh, I hadn't thought of that,' Rosemary moans. 'It's my first Christmas off in three years. If I get stuck in this spot I'll do myself in.'

Rosemary moans again when we enter the classroom. An untimetabled Fat Jack is sitting at the front waiting to teach us – though in reality that is the one thing he hardly ever does. Today is supposed to be a lesson on 'leadership styles'. A few minutes into the session and Fat Jack is staggering about with one hand at his throat, demonstrating how he struggled, at some stated time in his nursing career, with what sounds like the biggest, toughest, most psychotic patient in the history of mental illness. We look at one another; Rosemary shrugs her shoulders at me and shakes her head. I soon drift off, day-dreaming or doodling, anything but watch this embarrassing spectacle. We've all seen its various forms a hundred times before. Fat Jack struggles on without us. Deep down I feel sorry for him, but I can't forgive him for wasting my time like this.

Maisie soon falls asleep. Joanna, who's sitting next to her, keeps nudging her surreptitiously under the table, trying to wake her up again before Fat Jack cottons on. Luckily he's so engrossed with his present performance that he's incapable of noticing anything, staggering and rolling around the room in his renewed battle with the King of the Psychotics. The rest of us hide our faces in our hands, taking sly sideways glances at one another and trying to stop the laughter spilling out as Maisie slumbers happily at her desk and Fat Jack bounces idiotically around the room.

A sudden violent gripping of the bowel wipes the smile off my face. Fat Jack repeatedly ignores my raised hand and in the end I just have to get up and leave. I scamper crab-like from the classroom, down the corridor and into the toilets, pulling desperately at my trousers. As I enter the only cubicle at full speed my problems really begin!

The door won't close. A person in less distress could see that it was catching against the bottom of the frame. In my frenzied condition, hopping from one foot to the other like a chicken with burnt feet, this takes rather longer to work out. When I eventually twig on and grab the door in both hands to lift it the fraction needed to miss the frame, I'm racked by another violent spasm. The next moment finds me staggering forward out of the cubicle into the main toilet area with the door, which has jumped free of its hinges, clutched to my chest and my trousers dropping down around my ankles.

Barging around the toilets with my unwanted partner the cramping in my bowels worsens. The door gets heavier. I stumble over my flapping trousers and crash into some lockers. On the rebound I put one foot into the gulley at the bottom of the urinals. I am not amused, a stagger later, to see myself reflected bare-arsed in the mirror above the sinks. The noise of all this is incredible. I'm sure that at any moment the main door will fly open and I'll be indelibly stamped into hospital legend as a door fetishist. I can't believe this is happening to me. Eventually I manage to steady the door by resting it on my feet. Then, shuffling like some distraught penguin, the door still balanced on my toes, I back across to my starting point.

When I finally make it back to the classroom Joanna has succeeded in waking Maisie up. Outside the snow is falling thick and fast again, blowing hither and thither in the steadily rising wind. Fat Jack, still animated, is telling a favourite story of his, the one about the brilliant student nurse with a first-class degree in theology whose hair he washed every day in the school to cure him of head-lice. As he talks he acts out a little pantomime of washing the student's hair. 'He couldnae have been that bright,' points out Maisie, 'if he ended up with a load of nits because he couldnae wash his ain hair!' Fat Jack crumples, tries to bluff his way out, then draws the lesson to a premature close, departing in a huff, supposedly to keep an appointment. 'Could ya imagine letting him wash yer hair?' Maisie exclaims, pulling a face and shuddering. 'No thank you.'

'Oh, it makes me so mad,' says Joanna peevishly. 'We never get taught anything in this place. Look at it, half an hour still to lunch and the lesson's over. And what did he tell us, nothing! Just a load of rubbish about some blinking nits. How are we ever expected to pass our finals?' 'Dinnae get yer knickers in a twist, hen,' advises Maisie philosophically. 'Just look at some of the cretins that work here, the exams cannae be that hard. They passed.' She rocks back on her chair, content with her contribution to the debate, and raps Rosemary around the back of the head with her ruler. Rosemary, after tipping over the rocking Maisie, announces to the room at large: 'Oh I'm starving.' 'You big fat pig, Rosemary!' Maisie shouts at her from the floor, then, scrambling to her feet, gesticulates to the rest of us: 'Do you know what she had for breakfast? A big fry down the canteen, a chocolate bar from the shop on the way back, and then she ate half a trifle in the flat before coming here.' 'I did not,' Rosemary defends herself, though only half-heartedly. 'There was only a bit of trifle.' 'Aye, and that's only a bit of bum, I suppose,' jokes Maisie, pointing at Rosemary's posterior. 'Oh don't, Maisie,' cries Rosemary; then, looking over her shoulder, she agrees: 'God, my arse is getting enormous!' She pulls and clutches at herself as if to confirm her worst fears. 'It's like the hump of a camel, that arse,' says Maisie, 'You could live off it for months.' Rosemary closes in and a good-natured scuffle ensues.

Mr Gerard, another of our tutors, comes to take the next lesson and we all breathe a sigh of relief. Especially Rosemary, who is busily engaged in giving Maisie's ears a vigorous rub as he walks into the room. Maisie, who, not surprisingly, hasn't heard him come in, is shouting at the top of her voice, 'Get off my bloody ears, you cow!' 'Shall I come back when the bout's over?' Mr

Gerard asks, smiling. 'Or do you want me to stay and referee?' At least he has a sense of humour. He needs it for the film he shows us. 'Is that your Ma, Buster?' Maisie shouts back to me, as a nurse who wouldn't have looked out of place in the Crimean War appears on the screen. The uniform is ancient, starched bib and all, while the furniture looks prehistoric. An unfortunate patient of obese appearance comes into shot, rather blurred. 'It's Fat Jack,' howls Rosemary, 'getting his catheter in.' 'Look, even his willy's fat!' adds Maisie, dissolving us into fits of laughter. The old film scratches and bounces along until in the end even Mr Gerard can't stand it any more and turns it off to a subdued cheer.

After lunch I trudge back up the same path I saw Tim on in the morning. But now the snow is pushing up across it, drifting against the hedge on one side, and I have to lift my feet clear to make any progress. The weather has been terrible lately, and though they've managed to keep the main road open into town, where I live, many of the staff have been unable to get in to work.

Fat Jack catches me as I stand in the hallway of the school knocking snow off my clothes. He looks agitated. 'Could you spare me a minute please? I've had some bad news.' As he speaks his arm is on mine, gently, insistently, leading me towards the privacy of his office. I know straight away what's wrong. My sister-in-law has been seriously ill for several months and I suppose she must have died. Fat Jack knows all about it because I've already had some compassionate leave. I feel shaky, even though it's expected, and am grateful to him for his support. He's not such a bad old stick. 'Sit down, son, sit down.' He motions towards the chair in front of his chaotic, paper-strewn desk, walks to the window as if drawing himself together, then turns to face me, a look of anguish upon his face.

'Bunty's had a fit!' he suddenly bursts out, wringing his hands together in an anguished fashion. For a moment I'm completely nonplussed. Who do I know called Bunty that's epileptic? My mind races through the family tree but there is nothing there. Fat Jack continues: 'My son's just been on the phone to tell me.

My wife's in a terrible state – we both think the world of that little animal.' I sit there stunned as realization dawns. 'His cat, his pet cat!' I think. 'He's on about his bloody cat.' Fat Jack confirms this suspicion by performing a mime of what the cat looked like while having its fit. 'I've got to go home,' he goes on 'but there's nobody around at the moment I can tell. Would you let Mr Gerard know for me when he comes back from lunch?' I find myself weakly nodding my head. He has already picked up his raincoat and briefcase, and I feel again that pressure on my arm as he quickly ushers me out of his room, locks the door behind him and leaves.

The domestic lady finds me in the corridor. 'Where's that podgy shyster off to in such a hurry?' she asks. I struggle for a moment before I can concentrate enough to tell her. 'Don't tell me he's burying that bloody cat again!' she cries. 'The poor old thing has a fit every time he wants to get off early. He's been getting away with that for years.' Hanging up her coat she adds as an afterthought, 'It's the snow. He's frightened of getting stuck here, that's why he's cleared off home. He'll get stuck there instead, the crafty devil.' She makes us both a cup of tea and we sit in her kitchen drinking it, surrounded by the steam from the boiler which mists up the windows.

'Listen to this,' Maisie shouts across from her desk in the library, where we have gravitated to do private study in the absence of our tutor – a common occurrence. She has some sort of dictionary open on her desk and now reads aloud from it: 'Fart – the cry of an imprisoned turd.' She rocks about in her chair laughing, as we all look up and grin at her. 'That Joanna must have a few prisoners,' Maisie rabbits on, 'judging by the stink in our kitchen this morning.' 'Maisie Campbell!' Joanna protests. 'You little fibber! I did not – you know – do anything in the kitchen. What a thing to say about anyone!' She laughs, looking towards me, and adds, 'The little get!' We're both pleased to see Maisie looking happier today. She's been getting a hard time in the hospital lately, sent to Coventry by some staff, threatened by others, all for reporting a charge nurse for abusing patients. I guess she's glad to be out of it for a while. Not that she's one to reveal her feelings.

Maisie returns to her dictionary, happy to have wrecked everyone's concentration, and continues to read little snippets aloud to the rest of us. An amusing definition of bestiality is interrupted by the door opening, and her voice fades away at sight of the florid-faced Mr Neale, one of our more senior nursing officers, and Mr Gerard. 'Could I have a word, please?' Mr Neale requests, not smiling. Maisie gives him a sick, ingratiating grin. 'Do you think he heard me?' she whispers to Joanna as we file through the door behind the two men. 'I should think the whole hospital heard you,' Joanna kids her in a loud voice. 'Shush – oh dinnae say that!' beseeches a mortified Maisie. 'I'll die if he says anything to me.'

It isn't Maisie that Mr Neale's after, to her obvious relief, it's all of us. He indicates the continuing snow outside the window: 'Apparently this bad weather is going to get worse, and we're already short-staffed on most wards with so many people snowed in at home. I know you shouldn't be expected to give up school to help out but the situation is pretty grim, and in the absence of' – he looks around as if anxious – 'Fat Jack' – we laugh at his use of the nickname – 'Mr Gerard has agreed to let me approach you to ask if you will help cover the wards.' We all look at one another. Everybody's thinking about our Christmas holidays. After a respectful pause Rosemary pipes up. 'Well, I'm quite happy to help. Anything to get out of this dump.' Mr Gerard rolls his eyes to heaven. The rest of us nod or murmur our assent. 'But what's going to happen if it's still like this at Christmas?' Rosemary asks. 'We're all supposed to be on holiday, you know.' 'Let's worry about that a little later in the week,' says Mr Neale. 'Nobody's going to keep you here against your wishes, but if the weather stays like this I would have thought those of you from away are going to have a hard job getting home anyway.' He doesn't need to labour the point as all our eyes swing involuntarily towards the weather outside the windows.

'OK then,' continues Mr Neale, after settling a few other queries. 'Here's what we'll do. I'm going to use you to cover the wards as and where the need is greatest. I understand all of you but one actually stay in the Nurses' Home here at the hospital, so I can be sure you can physically get to work. I won't ask you to fill in on any wards that you haven't already worked on, but you may well end up working on different wards each day.' 'How do we know where we're going to be working if we're just filling in?' asks Rosemary. 'Just report to the Nursing Office at the start of each shift,' Mr Neale replies. 'They'll be able to tell you where to go.' 'Aye, they've told me where to go a few times,' whispers Maisie to me behind her hand. 'Now,' Mr Neale continues, 'my first problem is covering the acute wards tonight. Can any of you help me out?' Joanna and I volunteer. Joanna likes nights and I need the money. He sends us away to try and get some sleep before starting work in eight hours' time.

As we walk away from the school I pretend I'm going to the Nurses' Home to kip with Joanna. 'Get off home, you daft bugger,' she laughs. 'And wrap my present up.'

There are no buses at this time of day – they run to coincide with shift changes – but if you sit at the bus stop somebody you know will usually give you a lift. Today George picks me up. I've known him since my first day here, a fellow student but a little further on than me, with his finals in January. His face looks drawn and haggard and I guess he must be putting the hours in studying. He's certainly not his usual self and seems preoccupied about something, hardly saying anything to me during the trip. 'Come round one night and I'll buy you a pint,' I tell him as I get out, but he doesn't answer, roaring off before I've even got the door closed properly.

Back at the house there's the kitchen full of dust behind a perspex screen and the sound of some serious hammering from the builder. My wife, Anne, is on her knees painting the skirting-board in the front room. It seems as if we've been doing this house up for ever, and we're both sick to the back teeth of holes in the floor, having no bedroom and constantly chewing dust. Pacing the renovations to match our salaries has only dragged the whole job out and it is now nearly two years since we started pulling the place to bits. She presents me with another endless stream of bills and we go upstairs to talk where it's quieter.

No rooms up here any more, just an empty shell with one big wooden beam somehow holding everything up. We're living in the attic. I ask her how her sister is but she can't talk about it. She's just bottling it up, waiting, Christmas making it worse. I start to tell her what Fat Jack did to me, then think better of it. Instead I tell her why I'm home early and we skirt around all the raw areas. She shows me the Christmas presents she's bought for the family and I make the appropriate comments, thinking what a hard time she's having with the house the way it is, her sister so ill and the weather so lousy. 'I had to take the Christmas tree down,' she tells me quietly. 'It was ruined with the dust.' The guilt for putting her through all this twists into me and I lie awake in bed through the long dark afternoon, unable to sleep, wondering why I gave up a well-paid job to become a student mental nurse.

The day staff, four of them, are sitting around a table at the nurses' station. They could have been there an hour or more. If you didn't know it, like I did, from working here on days, you could guess it from the pile of fag ends in the ashtray, the plate with one mince pie left on it, the stained mugs with the slops of cold tea in the bottom, the *Daily Mirror* opened to show a nearly completed crossword. My arrival, which heralds their departure, is the signal for general movement.

The night staff nurse, Joan, auburn hair raked back from her broad forehead and up into a bun, dominates the nurses' station as soon as she arrives. We also get an auxiliary, who is an unexpected bonus. The three of us go into Sister's office for the report. Hard to think of Nikki as a Sister though, changed already to go out on the town, in a black leather mini-skirt with matching boots, fishnet tights and a red shimmering top of some material unknown to me. The henna hair is spiked up and lacquered into position, the nails brightly dangerous with polish, the make-up heavy. There's a thin gold chain around the waist. I like it.

Nikki gives the report quickly, in a hurry to get away. 'Well you know most of them, Joan. We've had Dr Garsby re-admitted today, she's been a bit high lately and Dr Jones wants to get her stabilized again. Apparently she got a bit excited this morning and turned a few tables over in the dining room. We've got her in the first side room, on constant observation, but she hasn't been any trouble to us this afternoon. All the furniture has been taken out. She's had some intramuscular Largactil this morning at nine o'clock, as well as her oral medication, and that seems to have settled her down. The rest of them are fine and the five for ECT in the morning are marked on the board, if you could just make sure they have nothing to eat or drink, please.'

I groan inwardly at the combination of Emma Jane Garsby and Largactil. Largactil: a 'major tranquillizer', we call it, or a 'neuroleptic', or a 'phenothiazine', depending on who we're talking to and how much we want to impress them. The patients refer to it more simply as the 'liquid cosh' or the 'chemical strait-jacket' – which is how they experience it and the many other 'major tranquillizers' now available.

The old-timers on the staff often talk of the miraculous cures they witnessed when Largactil was first introduced: patients who had been unmanageable for years being discharged home within days or weeks of first receiving the drug. Perhaps it was like that. For me, 'major tranquillizers' are day rooms half full of sedated patients; a trained nurse pushing up my elbow as I pour out a prescribed dose of syrup, winking and saying, 'Just let your hand slip a bit with that one, son, and we'll have a nice quiet shift.' They're an old man of 80 rendered unable to walk by too high a dosage; a middle-aged woman with hideous tongue and facial movements, a side-effect from prolonged use. But worst of all, in an overstretched and understaffed NHS, these drugs can become the only long-term treatment a patient ever gets. If you're not a problem in a mental hospital you're not anything. Just someone slowly drowning in a sea of tranquillity.

I can't say I'm surprised to see Emma Jane Garsby in again. Manic-depressives tend to need frequent re-admissions for stabi-lization of their mood-swings, especially when they have only recently become ill. That doesn't make it any easier to accept, though. The first time I worked on this ward she was here as a doctor. An attractive young woman I'd really taken a liking to, especially as she lacked the usual arrogance I had learnt to associate with the medical profession. The second time I worked on the ward she was here as a patient. To say it was a tragedy would be glib. For her and her husband it was the end of everything.

A fellow student brings in our tea, her last job of the day, and rushes off to get changed. I remember there's a party on tonight in the Nurses' Home. The auxiliary pours a cup for me and Joan, then goes off to take over observation of Emma Jane. 'What does she look like, dressed up like that?' Joan asks me, about Nikki of course. 'No wonder men get funny ideas about nurses!' 'They would if they saw me dressed up like that,' I joke, and we have a laugh together, which is a good start to the night.

On Acutes at night you can usually do as much or as little as you like. Being a student, you follow the lead of your staff nurse. We sit in Sister's office and drink our tea. Not checking the patients or saying hello to them. They are due a cup of tea at 9.30 but make their own. The only help we give them is to unlock the kitchen door. The telephone rings a couple of times – the night staff off the other wards arranging who is going where for the meal-break and who is covering for who. It seems I'm going to the other acute ward while the staff nurse there comes across to have his break with Joan. It crosses my mind that he's giving her one as I listen to her chatting him up. Somebody phones to arrange mealtimes with the auxiliary and I act as go-between for Joan on the phone and the auxiliary ensconced with Emma Jane.

The auxiliary, a petite middle-aged lady whose name I don't know, is sitting on a hard red plastic chair in a corner of the side room looking at a dress pattern. A single dull night-light burns overhead in the high ceiling; the only other furniture is a mattress on the floor which gives the room the disreputable air of a squat. On this lies Emma Jane. She has thrown off the covers to get some relief from the stifling heat of the windowless room. I'm reminded once again that Emma Jane is extremely attractive, which somehow makes it seem worse that she should be here, her beauty in poignant contrast with her situation, as if one had caged a bird of paradise.

When our mealtimes have been sorted out I sit back down in the office with Joan. There is a feeling of strength about her, probably from that straight back and those square shoulders. We sip our tea and she tells me that she hates the job and works nights because she earns more and sees less of the patients. In the time before we start giving out the night medication at ten o'clock, Joan sits and tells me stories about the hospital and the people who live and work here. All illusions are shattered as the personal lives of even the more respected senior colleagues are exposed to Joan's clinical character assassinations.

'He's no cause to talk,' says Joan about one of our nursing officers who has been complaining about standards of behaviour in the Nurses' Home. 'I worked on the wards with him when he was still a staff nurse. One late shift him and her, you know who I mean, that auxiliary, came on for a night shift together. Well, I've set off home and got most of the way there when I realize my door-keys are still in my uniform in the cupboard. So then I have to trail all the way back to this bloody dump – what a temper I was in! Of course back on the ward there's no sign of either of them two – not that it bothered me; all I wanted was my keys and to get off home to bed.' She laughs but stifles it. 'Well, I charge into the main room and all the old fellows are still wandering about. "Funny," thinks I. "This lot should be in bed by now." Anyway, I'm in too much of a hurry to dwell on it. Instead I yank open the cupboard door so I can get my keys out of my uniform.' She puts her hands up to her face as if physically holding back the laughter. 'Well, what a shock I got! Who's in there going at it hammer and tongs like a pair of bloody hunchbacks but them two! I mean to say, in a bloody cupboard.'

'What happened to get David the sack?' I ask Joan a bit later. 'One minute we're in school together and the next he's gone.' Joan sniffs disapprovingly. 'That daft sod,' she says. 'He was screwing one of the patients, that Mary Chambers, serves him bloody well right.' 'Mary!' I exclaim. 'God, she must be nearly

50!' 'Well, everybody thought something was going on, but nobody could catch them misbehaving. Then one night when Mary's on leave, her old man decides to follow her because he thinks there's something going on as well. Result is he finds them having it off in the back of David's car. There's a little fracas, the police are called, and that, as they say, is that. He gets his marching orders. Mind you, he should have known better than to muck about with Mary, she's a real manipulative bitch. She was just using him for her own ends.'

I think about David and the waste of it all. About his wife and children and the misery of their Christmas. About how nothing is ever black and white. Joan runs through the patients on the ward for my benefit but I already know most of them, all fully paid-up members of the 'Magic Roundabout'.

Long before ten the first patients drift up to form a queue outside the clinical room door. By the time we get up from our tea and go through to dish out the tablets, at about five to ten, they are all lined up against the corridor wall, bar a tiny old lady called Edna, who is dementing, and one young paranoid girl who thinks everybody is trying to kill her.

Joan identifies the tablets prescribed and I dish them out from the various bottles and packets we keep in the trolley. Many patients have their own ritual for swallowing tablets. For most patients, and many staff, the drug round is overlaid with a quasi-religious devotion. Tablets are revered as if they were the Host itself; the wise nurse looks down benevolently upon the sinners who take their medicine, reaffirming their belief in the system.

Joan reads out a name and I look up with surprise, not realizing this person is still a patient. The woman facing me is a middle-aged lady done up to the nines, dyed raven hair piled high upon her head, false eyelashes, purple varnished nails. She looks like a contestant for the 'Glamorous Granny' title. Her name is Mary Chambers. Joan and I exchange furtive grins behind the upraised lid of the drug trolley.

Mary is in and out of here like a waiter through a kitchen door. I can't tell you the number of times I've nursed her, admitting the discharging her over and over again. Sometimes on the same day! Tonight she complains that the tablets are not doing her any good. 'Right, well don't have them then,' says Joan, reaching in her no-nonsense way to take them back. Mary quickly changes her mind. She will take them after all. But they give her such a headache. Already she is changing tack, having lost round one to Joan.

Walter, a well-built 50-year-old, is suffering from a bout of depression brought about by the loss of his leg. He doesn't look at me as I hand over his anti-depressants, which he needs coaxing to swallow. His whole posture is one of defeat; the slumped shoulders and bent back seem to bear a weight too great for them to carry. 'Do you need anything to help you go to the toilet?' Joan asks, knowing constipation and depression often go hand in hand. Walter looks up at her, his head rising slowly as if being dragged back by some enormous gravitational force. The eyes stare coldly in Joan's direction. 'You'd need a stick of dynamite to clear me out,' he enunciates slowly. 'I'm blocked up solid from me arse to me Adam's apple.' There's a snigger from the queue behind him. 'We're a bit short on dynamite,' Joan tells him, at the same time reaching for the laxative mixture. 'Try some of this instead.'

The paranoid girl arrives after we shout repeatedly for her to come in from the corridor. I pour ten millilitres of Largactil suspension into a pot. She looks at it, then takes it from me reluctantly. 'What's it for?' The suspicion is tremendous, almost a physical force. She thinks everyone is trying to kill her. 'Just drink it up,' Joan tells her firmly, doing nothing to allay her fears. She is not in the habit of discussing medicines with patients. Under Joan's strong gaze the girl raises the cup to her lips. She swallows tentatively but then gags and spits it all back out on to the floor, hurls the pot from her and rushes from the room. I start to move after her. 'Leave it,' Joan says, unflustered. 'We'll do her last.'

Mary fetches Edna in for us, trying to get back into favour. Edna, 84 years old, four feet six inches tall, is ranting on about trumpets. We push her medication repeatedly towards her, try changing it from tablets to liquids, but she fends us off. In the end we give up, marking it down as refused. 'I've got to get home,' she tells us, but she doesn't know why. We go to get the paranoid girl, but in the whole maze of the acute ward we can't find her. The windows have only six-inch openings. We guess she's squeezed out of one of these and done a runner, yet it hardly seems possible. 'Bloody great, that's all I needed,' curses Joan. I nod my head as if agreeing but think of the girl, out there somewhere in the wintry night.

The night nursing officer tries to save us some trouble and searches the hospital buildings for her. It's no good though, she's clean away and the police need to be alerted. As the phone rings at the other end Joan and I try to remember what the girl was wearing. The police will want a description. We don't even know what she was like on the outside, never mind the inside.

After finishing medicines we go and see to Emma Jane. She is taken to the toilet by Joan and the auxiliary, who go in with her while she uses it. My job is to strip and remake the mattress, as the bottom sheet on which she has been lying is soaked with sweat and needs replacing. It's an awkward job to do on your knees but I've finished when they come back. In some strange way it helps me to be able to do something for her, no matter how small. She has another dose of Largactil, which is really starting to hit her now, so that she crashes out straight away between the clean sheets. 'Shut the door but don't lock it,' Joan tells me. 'She'll be OK now.' The door is big, heavy, solid, wooden, with a spyhole in the centre. Built to contain people.

Next it's Edna to be put to bed. She smells of stale urine. Joan washes between her legs and the auxiliary dries. I turn back the bed. 'I've got to go home,' states Edna. 'What for?' asks Joan. 'Because they're trying to kill me with them trumpets,' Edna replies, putting her hands up for them to slip the nightie over her head. The bed is too high for her to climb into and the two of them heave her up and then roll her over on to her side, tucking her in tightly.

The rest can get themselves to bed. Many have gone there direct from getting pills, the only thing that keeps them up until ten o'clock. It's time for us to have another cup of tea. As we drink Mabel comes and stands in the doorway. She mumbles to herself, just loud enough for us to hear: 'It's no good, it won't do any good. I'm bad. I'm all bad.' We do not answer, or even acknowledge her. Neither of us has the skills to deal with her effectively so we save face by not dealing with her at all. She hangs around a little longer, hoping to pull one of us in, then heads back down to the TV lounge. Electro-Convulsive Therapy for her tomorrow.

At eleven o'clock Joan sends me to clear the television room. The group of patients in front of the TV set, all the regulars, two of them lovers, look up at me and then look back at the TV. 'Time for bed,' I say. They continue to ignore me. 'Come on,' I repeat. 'It's time for bed.' 'Oh, let's just see the end of this,' asks Mary, smiling her manipulator's smile. Trouble is, I think they should be allowed to stay up as long as they like and the hospital system doesn't. They play on my being a new face. 'OK, just until this ends then.' I walk out feeling defeated.

'Did they go all right?' asks Joan. Now I'm trying to save face. 'Er, there's a good programme on they wanted to watch the end of, they're going after that.' Joan looks at me; she knows very well what happened. 'Go and tell them to go to bed,' she says. In the TV room nobody has moved. I feel lousy about asking them to go to bed until I notice they've changed channels and the lovers are curled up in a dark corner together. I unplug the telly and stand in the doorway until they've all trickled out past me like naughty children. Already I'm thinking, 'What a way to treat adults.'

The phone rings. 'The police are at the front door. They think they've got your patient,' the night porter informs me. I go to get her. 'Is this your missing patient?' a big copper asks me. I can't see from the door, as the girl is sitting next to a policewoman in the back of their four-wheel-drive Range Rover, so I go out into the ever-deepening snow to check. 'Yes, that's her.' 'Thought it was,' says the copper. 'You don't get many folks out in T-shirts on nights like this.'

We spend five minutes trying to get her out of the car but she refuses to return to the ward. At last the policewoman gets things going by pushing the girl out of the car from behind. I and one of the two male coppers grab her emerging body and 'help' her towards the door. She balks again and the blanket they've wrapped around her shoulders falls to the ground as she struggles. The other officer applies a bit of pressure from behind and the three of us gently manhandle her back down the main corridor to the ward. I wave cheerio to the coppers and lock the door with Joan's key.

The appalling thing is that the girl's an informal patient. She came here voluntarily. We have no legal right to detain her. Which makes a pretty sick joke of what has just happened. If she tries to leave again she will be put on a Section, that is, she will be held under one of the sections of the Mental Health Act. There's one ready made for the job, Section 5, for the detention of an informal patient already in hospital. Informal sounds so much better than voluntary. After all, people might ask awkward questions if they realized hospitals can detain voluntary patients. What is voluntary about it if the moment a patient tries to leave they are put on a Section? Mind you, a Section 5 is only for a maximum of 72 hours. But that can easily be converted to a Section 2, which is for 28 days, or a Section 3, which is for six months. How would our paranoid girl like that? Come in for a 'rest' the doctor tells her, and next thing she's in for six months! And she doesn't just walk away at the end of her six months like they do in prison. No, she has to get someone to discharge her. If her psychiatrist doesn't you can be sure the hospital managers won't. Then she would have to appeal to the Mental Health Review Tribunal. How about that for a scenario? Comes in voluntarily and now she's appealing after six months to be let out. What's more, if they don't think she's fit for discharge they can keep her another six months. For an endless number of six month's. In fact, she might never get out again.

All this could happen to the girl I'm walking beside now. So what has she done to deserve it, this possible life sentence? Well, she's paranoid, thinks everybody is trying to kill her. Which makes her life extremely difficult. But she hasn't threatened anyone, hasn't committed any crime, hasn't hurt herself. She's here because of what she might do. Would she be better off out in the snow? Or at home with a family that had her admitted here because they couldn't cope with her behaviour? I don't know the answer. All I know is a young girl is being held against her will, because of something she may do at some indeterminate time in the future, under a Mental Health Act that doesn't even define what mental illness is. For how can anyone define an illness of the mind when the mind itself is a myth?

'That was a daft trick,' Joan says when we arrive back at the office, getting to her feet and picking up the medicine keys. 'Now come and take your medicine and let's have no more nonsense.' Joan leads the way to the clinical room where the drugs are kept; the girl follows, with me behind the two of them. Joan measures out a dose of Largactil: it looks like a big one. 'I'm not going to take that,' says the girl. She backs away from Joan, but I'm in the doorway and there is nowhere for her to go. 'All right then,' says Joan. 'I'm not going to fight with you.' The girl looks relieved until she sees Joan getting out a syringe. Joan withdraws it slowly from its wrapper and fits on a needle. The needle looks long and sharp. 'What's that for?' the girl asks, wide-eyed. 'You,' Joan states simply. 'I don't want an injection. What do I need that for?' The girl is terrified, mesmerized by the sight of the needle. 'Look,' Joan says, stopping her preparations for a moment. 'You won't take your medicine. You have to have it, doctor's orders, so what else can I do?' The girl gives in. She swallows the sticky orange fluid in small reluctant sips. 'Come on.' Joan is getting irritated. She picks up the syringe again. The girl swallows the lot in one go, her eyes locked on to Joan's hands. She is the last one into bed.

It's midnight and the auxiliary has prepared the nurses' station. Clean sheets cover the chairs and the table. It looks like a setting for a seance, ghostly, somehow, in the dimmed lights of the ward. The older nurses won't sit in a chair unless it has a sheet on. It's the same attitude that has them refusing to drink out of cups patients have used, an unspoken fear of catching something, of ending up that way themselves. We have one Anglepoise reading lamp on our table, bent low to the cloth and giving off only a subdued light. In which the auxiliary is somehow making a dress, the pattern spread out on the floor at Joan's feet. 'It will be finished by morning,' she says. Joan takes out her knitting. I try to read a textbook without success. At one o'clock Alan, the staff nurse off the ward next to ours, comes across to have his meal-break with Joan. I go over to his ward to cover for him. The auxiliary goes off carrying a pillow to find a quiet room where she can sleep on the floor for an hour. If she's caught she will get the sack.

On Alan's ward Joanna is spending her night on duty. We have a laugh, Joanna and I, over cheese sandwiches and a pot of tea. 'Listen,' I say, cocking my head to the side and looking attentive. 'What was that?' Joanna strains her ears. Patients are snoring and coughing in their different rooms and dormitories, but she can't hear anything out of the ordinary. 'What is it?' she queries me nervously. 'I thought I just heard Joan and Alan hitting a simultaneous orgasm,' I joke. 'Oh you get, Buster,' she laughs, looking relieved. 'I thought something was really wrong the way you were carrying on. How could you do that to us?'

It's how the learners, mature or not, survive. On the laughs. I don't know what I'd do without the others in the group. Probably leave, like all the rest have who started out beside us three long years ago. Joanna's had a Christmas card from one of them which leads her indirectly into a story about Rosemary. 'I remember Rosemary getting the job of cleaning this old boy up once,' she reminisces. 'He'd been incontinent of faeces just about every-where and the smell was really awful. Anyway, she was gone for ages so as soon as I had a minute I went to see if she needed any help. When I opened the door, there was the old fellow standing in the bath wearing just a collar and tie. Rosemary had got this fag on the go, to hide the smell, and she kept running across and dabbing his legs with a wet cloth, then running back again to the other side of the room. Every time she approached the old fellow she stopped to blow a cloud of smoke all over him and moan, "Jesus Christ Almighty, you're killing me."'

'How's Maisie feel about going back on the wards?' I ask Joanna when we've recovered from the vision of Rosemary with the fag. 'I can't imagine she's overjoyed.' 'She's not,' Joanna agrees. 'Poor kid. Mr Gerard's told her she won't have to go back to you-know-where though, no matter what happens, so that's something. Aren't people rotten. She's only doing her job. I admire her for having the guts to complain. I don't think I could stick all that hassle.' She goes off to answer a cry from the female dormitory.

'Did you hear about all the stuff being nicked from the Nurses' Home?' Joanna asks, coming back. I nod my head. 'It's getting ridiculous,' she continues. 'People are losing cheque books, cheque cards, all sorts of things. And Lord knows what's going missing from Christmas cards. You know how daft people are, they all stick money in with them!' 'Have you got any idea who's doing it?' I ask. 'No,' answers Joanna, 'but the police were up this afternoon.' She hesitates, looks up at me and then away again, speaking in a quieter voice: 'They spent a lot of time asking Rosemary questions.' 'Oh come on!' I answer, startled. 'You can't be serious.' 'I don't think she's done anything,' Joanna says quickly, 'I'm just telling you the police were giving her a hard time this afternoon.' We leave it at that.

Tim comes wandering down the corridor from his side room. He's quite disturbed at the moment but sits and has a cup of tea with us, not that he manages to drink much of it, hallucinating freely somewhere between Mars and Saturn. It's hard getting through but Joanna and I both like him and try hard for a long time to establish some sort of contact. He really looks the part with his hospital pyjamas and his puppet-strings walk. Eventually he goes back to bed, though we have to remake it for him first. A real schizophrenic this one, right down to the twisted mess of knotted sheets that often seems to be their trademark on Acutes. As we work, Tim stands behind Joanna. He lifts his hand to his head as if trying to remember something important. 'You must come space-travelling with me some time,' he blurts out. 'It's burglefelt.'

Joanna and I sit down at the nurses' station again. 'It's burglefelt,' I say when she passes the tea. 'Just burglefelt.' We both laugh quietly; we wouldn't want him to hear us.

'Do you see much of George these days?' I ask her, thinking she's been out with him. 'What do you mean "see much of him"?' she retorts. 'I don't see anything of him. Not that I'd want to, he's getting really strange, that fellow.' 'Oh come on, he's not that bad,' I argue. 'Just a bit abrupt at times.' 'Huh, well you've not seen much of him lately then. I was down a female geriatric ward the other day and he's standing in the middle of the dormitory holding this old woman in his arms. Not doing anything with her. Just standing there holding her. Poor old thing must have been terrified. In the end they had to come and take her off him. I'm telling you, he's cracking up.'

'Never,' I retort. 'Probably just working too hard for his exams.'

'Get off,' Joanna answers. 'He's out getting drunk every night. He's not doing any revision at all.' I think of the George I met on my first day in this place, who gave me food and showed me the ropes, and the George I saw today, who helped me again but was a different person. A nagging doubt arises but it feels like disloyalty and I push it to the back of my mind. I suppose it's what we all fear most, crossing the great divide and joining the patients.

Maisie phones from the party. Drunk! She wants to talk to Joanna. Joanna doesn't mind and chats away while I do the crossword. Apparently there's been an altercation. I can faintly hear Maisie saying, 'I didnae start it, honest. They were all picking on me.'

'You can bugger off back to your own ward.' Alan's manner is always jocular. My eyes open: obviously I'd dropped off for a moment. 'Don't go sleeping on my sodding ward either, Student Nurse,' Alan intones, hands on hips like the nursing officer his voice is accurately imitating. He's hilarious and I get up to go a few minutes later still grinning at his repartee. 'That's right, bugger off out of it while I give this little classmate of yours a quick bang in the clinical room,' he commands. Joanna slaps the back of his head in protest and he slumps into the chair as if dazed by the blow.

Back on my own ward, the auxiliary is in the library sewing

together her dress. She gives me an apple. Joan and I switch the lights off at 3 a.m. and settle down in our chairs around the table. We wrap the sheets around us, our temperatures dropping in the early hours, the pair of us looking ghostly in the near-darkness of the ward. I doze and wake, doze and wake. My eyes are heavy, I'm totally disorientated. 'AGHH!!' The scream rips through the quiet of the ward and shatters me back to full consciousness. In the opposite chair Joan is now also wide awake. I can hear the auxiliary running down the corridor from the library. 'Where the hell did that come from?' Joan asks, but even as she speaks she gets her answer. 'HELP, GO AWAY, PLEASE HELP ME.' The last, drawn-out syllables in this desperate plea clearly come from the female dormitory.

Alice is posturing over Mary Chambers's bed. Poor Mary has woken up to a real-life nightmare. Alice stands on one foot, her other leg raised and bent at the knee, her arms held in front of her bent at the elbows, the hands like claws. Her whole body is bowed at the waist as she leans over Mary with a face hideously contorted in a horrific grimace.

Mary scrabbles to get out of bed on the side away from Alice. Alice makes no move to stop her. Mary is shaking all over. 'She's going to kill me, she is, she's going to do me in. Look at her. It's horrible. She should be locked up.' I don't think it's the right moment to point out that she is. Anxious voices come to me down the dorm; the ward is in uproar, other women screaming without knowing what they are screaming at. 'What's going on?' 'Who screamed?' 'I think it was Mary.' 'What a fright it gave me.' 'It's that daft Alice up to her tricks again.'

'Come on, Alice,' I say, getting hold of her arm and tugging her gently away from Mary's bed. Alice seems to come out of her reverie and notices me for the first time. She breaks away and runs off up the dormitory. The auxiliary, nothing if not a practical woman, puts the main lights on so we can see what we are doing. The door at the far end is locked and Alice stops tugging at it and turns back to us. 'I'll do a handstand if that will please you.' She looks confused. The auxiliary and I approach her slowly; Joan is calming Mary down at the far end of the dorm. Alice does a handstand. For a second I step outside myself and see the funny side of all this, especially Alice, everything on display, her nightdress tumbled down around her head, the other patients looking shocked but not looking away. Then we grab her. She fights and we run her down the ward to stop her hitting us. By the time we get her in the side room she has stopped hitting out and is just a little wild-eyed and breathless. Joan fetches the Largactil. Sometimes it seems like the whole world and its mother is on Largactil. Alice swallows it. The auxiliary fetches out all the furniture apart from the bed. We lock the door and leave the night-light on. The switch for it is outside in the corridor. I think how much that light would annoy me if the tables were turned. Already I feel guilty for having run Alice down here. There was no real need. Just my stretched nerves over-reacting to a situation I've never been trained to handle, when my body feels it should be at home asleep. It seems your self-control is much less at night.

Now we have to go down into the female dormitory and sort them all out. Mary is sitting at the nurses' station having a fag to quieten her nerves. We leave her for the moment to deal with the rest of them. This is where Joan's silent authority comes in so useful. There's something very reassuring about a person who's so sure of herself. She brooks no argument. Everybody goes back to bed. 'It's all right now,' Joan tells them. 'Off you go, back to sleep.' Anybody else in charge and they would have been having hysterics all night, but Joan only allows them a normal reaction, there is no room with her for manipulating events to suit themselves. As Mary finds out. She is just taking a second fag out of her packet as we get back to the nurses' station. She looks up. By her face I can see she is ready to make a night of this. 'Don't bother lighting that,' Joan tells her straight. 'Get yourself off to bed.' Mary doesn't like it. You can see the battle in her face. She wants to play up. Be histrionic. Be demanding. Be the centre of attention. But there's something about Joan that tells her it would not be a very good idea. Mary goes to bed.

Alice's voice drifts down the empty corridors, pleading to be let out. Her cries are interspersed with banging on the door.

28

Boom, boom, boom reverberates through the mad night, exaggerated by the silence of the ward. 'Of course you know it's a full moon,' the auxiliary informs us. 'That's what's wrong.' Lunatics! Perhaps she's right. There is something startlingly strange about the place tonight, a restlessness of shadows and things just outside my consciousness.

We're having another cup of tea to settle us down after Alice's little effort. I'm still drifting in my thoughts when the scuffling of bare feet hurrying down the corridor arrests me. Is it here and now or somewhere else? I turn in my chair to face the open door on to the corridor, the small hairs standing up on the back of my neck. Naked as the day she was born, long brown hair streaming out behind her, Emma Jane shoots past. One can see on her briefly glimpsed face that she doesn't believe this. The blue eyes wide and fearful. A whimper breaks loose from her throat. Joan and the auxiliary run after her. This is women's work. I protect myself from recrimination by staying put while they bundle her back to the side room. Emma Jane doesn't struggle much. The psychosis is dampened down by the Largactil and what she can't believe is her captivity again. In a mental hospital. Joan spends such a long time talking to her that I guess inside she still cares. Reassured, Emma Jane quietens down and goes back to sleep, despite Alice who continues banging on her door.

Going to check on Alice, I look through the spyhole, down that optically sucked-back length of room, to a hideous sight. She has found the mirror and is grimacing wildly at it. Demonic is the word that jumps to mind. A young woman in just a nightie, bare-foot, hissing at herself in a mirror, pulling her face in every direction at once, gums drawn back over snarling teeth. It makes me shiver.

We try to settle down once again, the auxiliary to her dressmaking, Joan and I to dozing and waking, dozing and waking. It makes me feel sick. When I'm at work like this I sometimes don't know if I'm actually asleep and dreaming of being at work, or at work and thinking I'm dreaming. My eyes jerk open and I am at work. Somebody is coming down the corridor. Somebody with confident footsteps. Not a patient! I kick Joan's foot. She grunts and opens her eyes as I switch on the light. The night nursing officer comes in to collect our reports. Joan sends me to collect those off the adjacent wards while the two of them have a cup of tea. On my travels I unlock a door and stick my head out for a breath of fresh air. Outside is delicious, a lunar landscape of fallen snow, the full moon icing everywhere with its milky glow, the motorway quiet. I take my time and listen to an owl hooting in a dead elm out in the park.

The nursing officer is set for a long chat with Joan. He tells us of the night's deaths. One of them I know, and a sadness grips me for the little old man who had the misfortune to live so long he wet himself and ended up in here.

Edna comes in looking for a needle. 'What do you want a needle for?' asks Joan, humouring her. 'To sew the raindrops,' Edna says. 'I just want to make a rainbow.' We put her back to bed, protesting. She gets up again. This happens several times. The nursing officer gets fed up sitting on his own and goes off on his rounds. I get fed up with Edna and Joan lets me go to get her medication, both of us knowing it will make her sleep all day tomorrow. I've nothing left in the way of persuasion. When I get back Joan is quietly shutting the door on a sleeping Edna. I feel inadequate and tell her so. Joan says she gave our young paranoid girl more than her prescribed dose of medicine. None of us can really cope.

The door-bell rings. Joan and I look at each other, both thinking, 'Now who the hell is this?' I go to answer it. Mary's mum is at the door and wants to see her daughter! I point out that it's the middle of the night but she is adamant. Joan comes to see what's going on and recognizes the mother as an ex-patient. She sends me to phone a taxi. The woman does not argue with Joan. When I've been standing around awkwardly with this dotty old lady for 40 minutes the taxi eventually comes. 'I've no money for a taxi,' Mary's mum tells me. Joan groans when I tell her. 'She could have said.' A quick phone call to the night nursing officer secures us £5 out of the emergency fund. Mary's mum is packed off home. As she goes Edna arrives, coat over her nightie and ready for the off. We spend five minutes trying to persuade her to go back to bed, then ten minutes trying to drag her back there. Eventually Joan says, 'Just let her wander for a bit, Buster, I'll go and get her medication.' Joan walks off to the clinical room and I follow Edna, feeling like one of the seven dwarfs as I trail along behind this tiny person. We go in and out of several side rooms, to the surprise of their occupants, through the bathrooms and the toilets and back down the dormitory before Joan returns. Edna refuses to take the syrup. Joan goes and makes a cup of tea which we get Edna to sit down and drink. The syrup is in the tea, of course. After another half-hour of walking up and down the ward Edna is sedated and we put her back to bed.

Emma Jane comes out of the side dormitory, her hand to her mouth. She vomits across the corridor in a graceful arc. Very spectacular. Joan helps her change while I clean up the sick, wondering on my hands and knees why it always seems to have carrots in it. In the library I can hear the auxiliary's sewing machine whirring away, not that we need her, it's just irritating when I'm working and someone else isn't.

Dawn finally arrives. Joan and the auxiliary go and check everyone is still alive. If the day staff find we have left them any bodies they will call us back from home to do the necessary. I pick up the sheets off the armchairs and throw them in with the used linen, then put the chairs back where they came from in the consultant's office. It takes a few minutes to drag the heavy chairs down the corridor but it's worth it for the extra comfort they provide in the night.

It's a long walk down the main corridor to the kitchen. I switch on the boilers and prepare a tray for the day shift – if any of them can get here – and a trolley for the patients. The gulls fight in the snow outside the kitchen windows for the old bread I throw them. Some of them are as big as dogs. When the water boils, bouncing about in the perspex boilers, I make the tea and leave it on the trolley in the corridor where the early risers can help themselves. Then it's tea for the day staff. If there's one thing you learn as a student nurse it's how to make tea. The tray is heavy and it's a long walk back up to the nurses' station.

There are a few patients about now; we drift past each other on the long, empty corridor. I remind those for Electro-Convulsive Therapy not to have anything to eat or drink. I can see what a killer that bit of information is. Get up early, desperate for a cup of tea and a fag, only to be reminded that it's not on. Walking around with parched lips, perhaps until eleven o'clock. They hate me for reminding them, yet they would blame me if I didn't.

The day staff start to arrive, armed with horror stories of road conditions. They gulp their tea and suck greedily on their fags as I wait for Joan to finish giving Nikki the report. The tiredness grips me, makes me irritable. I can no longer trust myself to think. The auxiliary shows me the completed dress but I feel nauseous and cannot even smile.

At last we can go. The day shift is still short of two nurses. A few late-comers straggle past me going in to work. I permit myself a quiet smirk. Behind me a crash. Somebody running. It's me! Beneath a car lies a porter and his bicycle. The porter worms out, he isn't hurt beyond some bruises but is badly shocked. We sort it out. The porter limps off with the driver. I follow with the bicycle, which has badly buckled wheels. 'Stupid old bugger,' curses the nurse who was driving, when she gets back to the car. 'Fancy coming to work in this lot on a bloody bike!' She has a point.

I have to sprint for the bus now. When I get on, other shattered night-shift nurses raise their head to give me tired smiles. There's only one thing in my mind, to see Anne before she goes to work. But it's not to be. The house is empty, my shouted greeting drifts back to mock me. Wearily mounting the stairs, closing the curtains, I get lonely into bed.

Thursday 20 December

The night staff look greasy-skinned with exertion and fatigue but still manage some banter as we arrive early on the ward. 'Don't tell me you two aren't sleeping together, getting in here at twenty to seven of a morning.' To which Maisie, who has also been drafted in here for the day, is more than equal. 'If he'd been sleeping with me he'd no be walking in, I'd be carrying the poor auld bugger.' The two male nurses are finishing off their last bed-round of the night, grinning now at this little red-headed barmpot. The foul odour of faeces is all pervasive. Around one bed the curtains are ominously closed.

Old Wilf comes and hovers over me, tall, thin and angular, repeatedly touching my cup to let me know what he wants. Putting him in a geriatric chair doesn't help. He looks askance at me and talks his gibberish. Once he spoke seven languages fluently. I give him some tea. A second later the cup crashes to the floor. Wilf looks startled and then laughs. He has a nice laugh and the corners of his mouth turn down when he smiles.

Maisie picks up the pieces of shattered cup with an ironic, 'Well done, Buster. I see you're on form today.' I fetch a mop and bucket. The night staff finish their round and one of them tidies away while the other makes a few hurried notes in the Kardex.

Bob Bates is already sitting up again behind his high cot sides, the thick swathe of iron-grey hair sitting incongruously atop his aged features. For a few moments he is quiet, then he grips the bars that surround him and gives them a rattle. 'Hey,' he shouts. 'Hey, let me out of here.' Nobody answers the call of just another old man, so he pulls himself unsteadily to his feet and stands swaying on the bed. With a muffled oath the nurse writing the

Kardex drops his pen and goes quickly down the dormitory to Bob's bed. Bob is trying to get a leg over the cot sides. 'Bob, Bob.' The nurse tries to get his attention, and gently shakes his arm. 'Bob, just have another five minutes' kip and then we'll get you up, eh?' His mate has gone to help. Together they peel Bob's gripping fingers off the cold, grey, metallic cot sides. He shouts even louder. 'Hey, come on, what are you doing?' He is starting to get alarmed. 'Help, police, help.' They force him down between the sheets, tucking him in so tightly that for the moment he cannot move, leaving him distressed.

In the next cot a dumpy figure has shuffled down the sheets and now sits with bare legs dangling through the bars at the end, his forehead pressed against them. He too rattles the cot sides but he does not shout. One of the night nurses jokes, 'He looks like he's driving a bus.' 'That's not funny,' Maisie tells him. 'Sorry,' he answers sarcastically, 'I'd forgotten you were such an angel.' Maisie bites her lip, not rising to the bait.

A few minutes later there's the sound of a loud thump and Bob is on the floor. He gets to his feet before I can reach him, apparently none the worse for his fall, and wanders down the dormitory towards me dressed in just a pyjama jacket. None of the incontinent old men gets pyjama bottoms to wear. I check him over then take him to the toilet, which is what he seems to want, judging by the way he's clutching himself. On the way we link arms and talk, though he doesn't understand many of the words any more. Bob jumps as his feet touch the cold toilet floor. Their chill stimulates him and he starts to pee down his leg. I reach my hands around him from behind and catch hold of his penis, pointing it at the toilet bowl. My tea is getting cold, but first Bob has to be washed and dried and put back to bed. He lies there smiling and laughing at me after he has been tucked in. I leave the cot sides down as all they do is cause the old men to fall from a greater height.

Maisie rushes past the end of the bed and Big Harry, still half asleep, is staggering down the dormitory trailing all his bedding behind him. 'Whoa, hold on, boy,' Maisie says, catching Big Harry before he trips. He wears his usual vacant expression, half hidden behind a ferocious stubble. She unravels the bedding, then takes him to the toilet. I hear her asking, 'Are ye wanting a pee?' And then her infectious laugh, followed by a single exclamation: 'Harry!' We're not officially on duty yet.

The rest of the day staff start to straggle in, everybody noticing those closed curtains. 'By, you bugger,' says Paul, the male SEN, catching sight of me. 'How did they ever capture you for another stint on this job?' I smile back at him. 'I heard you couldn't manage without me, Paul; anyway, you know it's my favourite ward.' 'Oh aye,' Paul laughs. 'Yours and mine too, eh.' He's fourth-generation Irish but carries the genes so well he could have just stepped off the boat. The tea is cold so another pot is mashed. There is a shortage of chairs and Davina, of the big white teeth and mousy pony-tail, perches on Robert's bed, waking him up in the process.

The night staff give us Report. As we'd known, behind the closed curtains lie the mortal remains of one old man, identified as Ron, who will not be opening any presents this Christmas. 'That's a nice start to the day then,' Paul says, raising his eyebrows expressively. After Report the night staff walk out of the dormitory past Blind Tommy's bed. He calls out, 'Where's ma fucking bottle?' They stop and give it to him. Tommy sits on the edge of his bed to use it. As he pees he starts to sing at the top of his voice in the darkened dormitory: 'Rule Britannia, Britannia rules the waves, Britons never, ever, ever shall be fucking slaves.' Paul says, 'That Tommy,' and we all know what he means.

'I'd better go and phone Ron's daughter,' Lynne, the Sister, says. She doesn't want to do it but she knows she has to. Our eyes follow her neat, trim figure down the ward until she disappears through the doorway. Paul sighs. 'What a bloody job that is.' We all nod in agreement.

A few minutes later Davina asks no one in particular, 'What's going on there?' We turn and look down the ward, following the direction of her gaze. Bob has got up again and is standing between his bed and Tommy's. I start to rise. Turning the wrong way, Bob tries to get into Tommy's bed. Tommy resists: 'Fuck

35

off, ya cunt.' Before anyone can move, Bob is belabouring
Tommy with punches to the head. I'm running down the length
of the dormitory. Reaching out to grab Bob my feet slide from
under me and we both go arse-over-tit and end up on his bed.
The floor is awash where he has been peeing up against his
locker, finishing the job off properly on his own. Paul comes to
check for injuries. Tommy has the beginnings of a black, blind
eye.

Eventually Lynne comes back and says, 'Well, I suppose . . .',
leaving the sentence unfinished. We all get up. It's our call to
battle. Somebody switches on the main lights. Those patients
getting baths have clean sheets on their lockers to identify them
and are left in bed to sleep on. We fan out down the ward, five of
us for 27 patients, the normal ratio despite the weather. Those
who are awake get tackled first.

I mop up Bob's pee from the floor with a towel so that nobody
else slips on it, then get Tommy's clothes out of his locker and
put them on his bed. 'There are your clothes, Tommy. I've taken
them off the hanger,' I tell him. He asks me who is on duty. A
trick of his to get attention. I tell him and his little blind head
listens closely, cocked to one side. 'Bought your Christmas
presents yet?' I ask. 'Wha' do I want them fuckers for?' he
answers.

Two beds up, Davina is getting Jake dressed. At five feet
nothing he fights her over every stitch of clothing. She talks to
him all the time with her nice soft Geordie accent. 'All right Jake,
let's get these nasty wet pyjamas off you now.' Jake is unimpressed and answers in a slurred Glaswegian bark, 'I don't care
what kind of fucking day it is.' He jabs a short right into her
belly: 'Leave me alone, you bastard.' He nips hard into her arm
making her squawk. Davina looks around for help and Paul
leaves Bob to lend her a hand. Together they wrestle Jake, head-
butting and kicking, into his clothes. They take him, still
fighting, off to the washroom for a shave. Bob, half dressed, gets
into a wet bed across the aisle and goes back to sleep.

Lynne is working in a small bay off the ward. Somehow she is
getting half a dozen of our better patients up at the same time.
Giving a helping hand to button up a shirt, or a word of advice

on tying shoe-laces; undoing a disaster with braces; telling Bert to get up for the hundredth time, then physically pulling him out of bed; pointing Little Jimmy in the direction of the toilet; stopping an old fellow from pulling trousers on on top of his pyjamas. Bert wants her to dress him. She refuses as he's still quite capable. He drops down on his haunches and tries to defecate on the floor in protest, going red in the face with the effort, but she catches him and pushes him through to the toilet. No wonder she has the odd grey hair. I would be no use here and look for quieter waters. Big Harry catches my eye as he moves.

Looking at Big Harry as he struggles up to a sitting position in bed I feel myself go pale. He is covered in shit! Sometimes one can be objective and think of it as faeces, or excreta. But this is definitely shit! It is spread on his hands, under his chin, over his pyjama top. How he's got in such a state in such a short time amazes me. Turning back the covers reveals more mayhem. I gingerly push him back down in the bed and cover him up again. 'Have a lie-in for a minute, Harry,' I tell him, thinking how best to go about getting him cleaned up. A bath, yes! But how to get him there? Paul provides the answer. A commode covered in a clean sheet appears. But first to fill the bath. I roll up my sleeves, shake a little talcum powder into the disposable gloves and pull them on. Plenty of bubble bath in the water to give some much-needed fragrance. Then back for Big Harry.

Everything is placed carefully in position around the bed. Paul turns back the sheets and pulls an involuntary face at the sight. Big Harry sits up stiffly and, with some help, swings his legs over the side of the bed. 'Oh no, there's crap on his feet.' Paul, quick as a flash, whips a towel in under Big Harry's descending toes. With great care, talking to him all the time, we pivot him on the towel and ease him back on to the commode, wrapping the clean sheet around his body to keep him warm. As I bend down to put his feet on the foot-rest, the appreciative Big Harry pats me on the head! I jump back but it's too late. The hand still held out is in the same condition as the rest of him. Paul retches. 'Come on, let's get him in the bath.'

The crowd in the dormitory through which we pass has

gathered momentum. Those without a nurse, and that's the majority, seem hopelessly lost. Some sit, half dressed, on beds, where the nurse has had to leave them to answer a more urgent summons, others have fallen back completely, yet more wander aimlessly around clutching bits of clothing or whatever they can lay their hands upon. Robert tries to help little Jimmy, his mate, who tells him to fuck off. 'Right-ho, champion,' Robert replies, continuing to try and help him. Blind Tommy is standing by his bed, dressed in just his vest and socks, belting out another filthy song. Those with a nurse are being either cleaned or dressed. The red plastic soiled-linen bag is looking well used.

Paul gets to the bathroom first. Without ceremony we unwrap Big Harry, grab an arm and a leg each and dump him in the bath. Then Paul runs out gagging to the toilets. I go over to the sink, fill it with water and stick my head in it. Washing my hair quickly, trying not to look too closely at the water in the basin. Feeling better a few minutes later when I'm rubbing my hair dry with a towel. Big Harry sits in the bath totally unconcerned, rubbing meticulously at a mole on his arm, as Paul throws up next door.

Picking up a wipe I get to work on Big Harry. Patches of white skin appear as he starts to emerge from his faecal disguise. The water becomes slimy. I pull out the plug and when the bath is empty rinse him off with an old plastic jug. Paul comes back and puts a towel over a hard-backed chair. We wrap another towel across Big Harry's chest and under his arms, for a good grip on his wet body, and then physically lift him out on to the chair. We have no hoist, but the hospital is cost-effective. Big Harry is dried quickly. Paul and I know exactly what we are trying to avoid: more of the same. Big Harry doesn't like the nappy. They are efficiently designed but still uncomfortable. He pulls at it and I have to hold his hands as Paul finishes dressing him. 'What a bloody morning this has been,' complains Paul from his position at Big Harry's feet. 'They're all either on the fly or crapped up.' His dark wavy hair is damp with sweat. Mine, I hope, is just damp.

The washroom, when I get there with Big Harry, is another

38

seething crowd. Old men being shaved, old men shaving themselves, old men looking at razors as if they had just been invented.
The electric razor buzzes, processing one after another. It is not
cleaned between shaves. Two lost souls are walking around with
ties looking for help. Jake staggers past me with Davina. His face
is cut from continually moving about while being shaved. He
looks rheumy-eyed and is not walking very well but still swears
at Davina, who, for safety's sake, is pushing him along gently
from behind and gripping both his arms. Jake jerks his head
backward and nearly catches her with it. Maisie laughs. 'You
auld bugger, Jake, behave yourself,' she says cheerfully. Jake
replies, his words slurred, 'Away and fuck yourself.' Maisie turns
to me, still smiling: 'Isn't he lovely?'

Shaving Big Harry is like cutting your hedge with a pair of nail
clippers. He has a beard like Desperate Dan and it takes two
disposable razors to get it all off. I fix him up with some braces
to stop his trousers falling down and take him through to the
dining room. The dining room crowd are all locked in on their
own. With our staffing levels we have little choice. Some of them
bang on the door to get out while new arrivals bang on the door
to get in. A voice shouts, 'Open this bloody door.' I go away and
worry about the myriad disasters that could occur to them,
unsupervised in their dementias.

Going back to the dormitory I meet Robert. He wanders down
the ward as if he were out for a stroll on the farm. Hands behind
the back, slightly stooped posture, flat cap on his head and
wearing a jacket despite the stifling heat. No, correction, he's
wearing two jackets. 'Morning, Robert,' I address him civilly.
'Come on with me a minute will you, there's something we need
to sort out.' 'Right-oh, lad,' he answers benignly, adding, 'I'll do
anything tha says.' We go back to the bed he sleeps in. 'Now
then, Robert, I think you've got a few too many clothes on.' I
start to undress him. He is wearing two jackets, the pockets of
which are full with socks and caps he has purloined on his
wanderings around the ward. Under the jackets he wears a
cardigan on top of a shirt on top of his pyjamas. I strip away the

layers. The trousers are difficult to remove. Under them are his pyjama bottoms and three pairs of underpants!

Once he's stripped down I start again to re-dress him. Robert helps, with that constant affable smile on his face that must have been his trade-mark throughout life. 'Champion, lad, just champion,' he keeps saying. A moment of suspicion arises when he can't put both jackets back on again. 'What's to do?' he asks quizzically. He watches me hang it in his locker and grunts approval as I show him his name on the outside of the locker. 'All right, lad, champion,' he says. It isn't even his jacket.

We walk down to the washroom through the continuing furore. 'By, there's some sad cases in here,' says Robert, looking around at the mêlée. Then he clears his throat noisily and ejects a mass of green phlegm on to the floor between the beds. Pointing out to him that this is not acceptable brings a blank look in reply but he answers with his stock phrase, 'Right-oh, lad, champion.' Getting it off the floor is rather unpleasant to say the least. Robert stands and watches me with interest.

In the washroom he shaves himself, doing better when I remove the cover from his razor blade. Every now and then he stops, clears his throat and gobs into the sink. Lynn is going radge. 'Robert, Robert, will you please stop doing that,' she snaps. He smiles at her. 'Champion, lass, champion,' he says.

In the emptying dormitory the beds lie covered in twisted soiled linen. Stripping them in pairs we engage in friendly competition. The skip fills with dirty sheets, draw sheets, pillowcases and pyjamas. Our movements become synchronized, like dancers. I work with Davina because we're both tall; she's telling me about her new flat. We slip into the rhythm. A blasting fart erupts from beneath the bedclothes of a sleeping Hugh. 'Better count his balls when we bath him,' Paul jokes, adding to the laughter.

Four still remain in bed. Those having baths. We tidy around them and they sleep on, oblivious to our presence. Some order is emerging. I find a top set of dentures in the dregs of a coffee cup but no clue as to who they belong to. Braces, bottles of urine, commodes, towels, trousers, coat-hangers lie scattered about the dormitory. We pick it up, hang it up, throw it in the skip, tidy it away, empty it, clean it. Maisie draws the curtains and we can open some windows for the first time today. Fresh air!

Maisie gets the job of mopping the toilet. 'How is it none of you men can pee in a straight line?' she asks, deliberately slandering myself and Paul by lumping us in with the old men. Paul gets her back, kidding her on about her red hair, and she chases him with the mop. The involuntary relaxation comes from knowing that the worst is probably over. Davina is in the washroom, shaving some stragglers. I tidy round her and get an earful of shaving cream for my trouble. Then Lynne comes in and says, 'Do you mind giving me a hand, Buster?' There's no need to ask what with. Davina pulls a 'bad luck' face in sympathy.

Ron lies on his back, on the bed, covered by the sheet. I get everything organized. Lynne comes back with the Death Box. There's no room for it with the two of us and the trolley round the bed so she leaves it on the next bed, outside the curtains.

'I'll shave him,' I say. Lynne nods. Turning back the top of the sheet to reveal his face has obviously upset her. 'This is awful,' she explains, a bit uptight, 'I've nursed him on and off for years, first on Acutes and then down here. He was a lovely little man when he was well.'

It's not so bad for me of course, only being here for the day and, in this case, not knowing him at all. If I have any feeling for him it's one of relief. Relief that he's out of this at last, without any more lingering, hopeless years to endure.

Tentatively I put some shaving foam on my hand and spread it evenly across the small amount of stubble on that drained face. Surprisingly he is still warmish to the touch. This makes the job easier for me. Shaving him I chatter on, as if he might give an answer. 'Just let me get this bit off under your chin, Ron. Won't be much longer now. Thank God the night staff remembered to put his teeth in,' I say to Lynne, shaving carefully around his mouth. She says nothing and I try to keep my stupid thoughts to myself.

Ron is soon shaved clean and Lynne washes off the soap and

dries his face. She also talks to him, gently and reassuringly. It isn't so bad now we've actually started. Lynne comes back with a bowl of fresh water. We turn the sheet down to his waist and pack towels around him. I wash, Lynne dries. Methodically cleaning him down. Right arm, chest, left arm. We move the sheet. Right leg, left leg, groin.

'Roll him to you,' Lynne directs. We both apply ourselves and he comes over easily. His back is all different shades of purple and seems almost soggy in texture. I guess it is just the blood draining down. Lynne washes his back and dries him while I hold him steady on his side. 'OK, over to me now.' My turn to wash and dry the other half of his back. It looks like a massive bruise.

'How's Maisie managing?' Lynne asks, partly I think to take her mind off what we're doing. 'You know what she's like,' I reply. 'She doesn't give much away about herself, always hiding behind the repartee, but I think it's getting to her. She certainly didn't expect the abuse and the threats. Not for reporting somebody for mistreating patients.' 'And why should she expect it?' Lynne asks vehemently. 'I mean to say, it is a hospital, the girl was right to report him.' 'But you know what they're like, Lynne,' I butt in. 'It's like the bloody Mafia. Some of them won't talk to her at all now and a few of them have been pretty nasty about it!' 'Well if I catch anybody saying anything to her,' Lynne says unsmilingly, 'they'll be for the high jump.'

Ron lies back on the bed. He is clean. Lynne goes for the Procedures Book. 'I haven't done this for a while,' she admits with a look that expresses her regret to be doing it now. 'Champion, lad, champion.' Robert's voice right behind me makes me jump out of my skin. He's walked in through the gap Lynne's departure left in the curtains. He looks unconcernedly about him. I pull the sheet back over Ron then take Robert to the dining room. Coming back I put the trolley outside the curtains so there is room for the Death Box. Lynne brings that in with the Procedures Book. She leafs through it quickly, then gets down to work.

First of all she takes some net bandage and cuts off a small strip. She ties it round Ron's penis and knots it in a bow. Next we tie the legs together at the knees and then at the ankles, making sure they are straight. Finally we tie his big toes together. It seems a daft, almost joky thing to do. 'At least there's no need to pack him,' Lynne says grimly as she works. 'I can remember when we used to have to pack every opening whether it was discharging or not.'

From out of the box she takes an identity bracelet, on which she writes Ron's full name. I have to go and find out his hospital number, which we add to the bracelet before clipping it to his wrist. The shroud comes out next. Full-length white plastic with a frilly ruff round the neck. It goes on fairly easily, if a little squeakily, and we roll him back and forth between us to get it wrapped around him, then tied together at the back like a theatre gown. Ron gurgles in his throat and we both look quickly up and then down again. 'Jesus!' Lynne says with some feeling. 'That's not funny.'

'Just a clean sheet,' Lynne directs. Again we roll him back and forth, first to get the soiled sheet out from under him and then to get the clean sheet spread neatly in its place. He lies there now, looking totally unreal in that awful cherubic shroud, like a choir boy suddenly aged. Lynne combs his hair neatly, enhancing the effect. Then we quickly wrap him up in the sheet, a big white human parcel that we seal up with long strips of Sellotape, pausing only to add his identity to the outside of it. Finished at last we clear away the trolley and the box, leaving Ron parcelled up behind the curtains. I phone the porters to come and fetch him.

Joy and Florrie, the cleaners, paragons of misery, are having a cup of tea when everyone goes into the kitchen. They look offended as the entire morning shift bursts among them gasping for a cup of something. Two middle-aged women who never thought they'd end up doing this for a living look sourly out from behind their fag smoke, particularly at Maisie, though they're too clever to say anything to her directly. Instead Joy says, 'They reckon that darkie – Rosemary is it? – they always have fancy names, don't they? Anyway they reckon she's the one been doing all the thieving up at the Nurses' Home.' 'You can't trust them, can you?' says Florrie, adding, as if to justify her statement, 'I can't stand them dirty black skins.' Lynne quells them with a look that would cut glass. 'Shut it,' she says. 'Unless you want me to do something about it.' The threat is real enough.

We sort out our drinks and take them down the ward to the office. Maisie's boiling. She knows what they're up to as well as I do. Needling her by getting at her mate. 'EEEEIHHHH!' She suppresses the scream, sitting in the chair, fists pummelling the arms to release her anger. 'Can you believe them two auld bitches?' she exclaims, near to tears now. I put my hand over hers. 'Sshh, don't let them get to you,' I say quietly as she gets herself back under control. We can hear, but not see, the old men, who are still locked in the dining room, and are safe from their pestering for a while. The smokers inhale deeply and calm their nerves. It's nine o'clock. Two hours' hard slog behind us and only a wardful of clean old men to show for it, and one of them's dead.

For minutes nobody says very much. Maisie, Lynne and Paul are smoking, sharing a common bond. Everybody slowing down, settling back into their chairs. It's against the rules, of course, but at the moment we don't give a toss. We all need a break. Lynne has just taken a first sip of tea when the doorbell rings. Paul goes and Lynne says a muted 'Bloody hell!' and stubs out her fag as Ron's crying daughter comes down the ward towards us. Lynne takes her into the office. We can hear the daughter howling from where we sit. Paul gets up and we all follow, leaving the full cups. Tea-break's over.

We're three quarters of an hour behind schedule, which is normal. Breakfast for the old men is waiting in a heated trolley. It's probably been ready for hours. The domestics have laid another trolley with all we need apart from tea. Davina mashes two pots the size of small buckets and adds the milk and sugar to them. Paul takes the heated trolley and I take the other. Maisie bustles on ahead, clearing a path through the doorway into the dining room. Somebody's peed over the rubber plant.

There's a general scrum around the trolley and we spend a lot of time sitting people down. Little Jimmy, seated, rubs at his forearm over and over again. 'But, but, but, but,' he repeats endlessly. Davina has started to lay the tables. The old men wrestle over the crockery and cutlery, moving it around, piling it up, anything but leave it where it should be. There are no condiments. Paul and I are diverted to sit Jake down – he has got up and started to wander. Jake still slurs his words but his mood has changed as if by magic. 'Could you show me the way to the toilets, please?' he requests with a smile. 'Certainly, sir,' Paul replies, following his lead. 'It's just this way.'

Maisie brings across the dishes while I remove the lid from the large stainless-steel container full of porridge, with which you could hang wallpaper. Davina adds two pints of milk to thin it down. The others scurry about serving, making sure everyone has a spoon to eat with, and that no one is using their knife and fork on the porridge. No one, that is, except Bob, who, stabbing out with a fork, keeps us at bay in between slurping his porridge noisily off the prongs. Maisie and Davina fix the long plastic aprons over the messy eaters. Paul comes back and starts pouring out the tea.

Bert grabs Wilf's porridge and there is an altercation between the two old soldiers. We move Bert and put him next to Big Harry. Soon Bert is taking sly spoonfuls out of Big Harry's dish as well as eating from his own, gobbling great mouthfuls down in huge gulps. Eventually he chokes and sprays the rest of the table with an obnoxious mixture of porridge and phlegm. Maisie good-humouredly reprimands him: 'Bert, will ye stop gulping your food down or you're going to be sick.' Bert grunts in reply and picks at the porridge on his jumper, putting the bits back into his mouth. Jake arrives back from the toilet to an empty dish. Someone has snaffled his porridge. We give Jake cereal. 'Thank you,' he says, like a proper little gentleman. Blind Tommy shouts, 'There's no fucking sugar in this porridge.' We add a few spoonfuls to his already over-sweetened dish. 'Fuck you,' he says.

Wilf pours tea into his porridge. It makes me sad to look at him, knowing his history, how he fought against Franco and fought against Hitler. His brother brought Wilf's medals in once

45

to show me, when I said I was interested, and hinted at another and much more secret service to which Wilf had once applied himself. His brother told me that after all the fighting Wilf went walkabout in the Australian outback to help him forget. And did I know Wilf had made his own films and collected birds' eggs, of which he had a whole roomful from all over the world? And that Wilf had once taken a job as a tea planter so that he might have a chance to find a particular specimen he wanted for his collection.

Every now and then Wilf tries to escape. He once hid all day, perfectly quiet, in the six-inch gap behind a wardrobe while we chased about frantically looking for him. I wonder where he thinks he is being held captive and what he reckons to his guards? I wish he could have escaped this cruel dementia instead of ending up here, slurping his porridgy-tea mixture from a spoon.

Paul and I clear away empty dishes. Maisie gets the cooked breakfasts out of the trolley and Davina unpacks the bread, spread last night, from its plastic cover. Each breakfast is covered with a metal lid. We take it off, drop a slice of bread on to the plate and dish it out. Some patients have special diets, but in practice they are indistinguishable from the ordinary ones. The gulpers get their food cut up by us. Paul spots the incorrigible Bert pinching food off Big Harry's plate with his fingers. He loses his rag: 'Come on, get out of it!' Bert doesn't move. Paul catches hold of his arm and tries to pull him up from his seat. Bert holds on to the table, which starts to tip over. I take his other arm to stop it. Together we haul old Bert to his feet and push him out of the dining room. He holds his hands to his head and moans as we lock him out, then stands banging on the door and peering in through the glass. Maisie opens the door and gives him out a piece of toast. 'Now behave yerself,' she tells him.

There's a choice of scrambled egg or black pudding and tomato. There's always egg. We run out of black pudding and then there's no choice. Bob wants black pudding and tries to take Wilf's. There is a brief flurry of blows before we can separate them and check the damage. Bob, struggling, gets moved to a different table. Wilf puts black pudding in his tea and eats the resulting mess with a porridge-covered spoon. A younger man, probably no older than 50, asks for more scrambled egg. He looks out of place in here among all these old men. His brain is prematurely pickled in alcohol.

Lynne comes in and shuts the door behind her, leaning heavily against it. 'Make her a cup of tea, please,' she asks Davina, 'and stay with her.' To the rest of us, still busy with breakfast, she adds, 'She wants to see him now. I'll have to go and unwrap the body.' Paul looks at her and slowly shakes his head from side to side. Lynne sends him off to get the trolley ready for the medicine round.

Everyone has had something to eat apart from the patients in bed waiting for a bath, who will get some tea and toast afterwards. I start to lead those who have finished back to the washroom, where we clean them up all over again. Then Paul and I start the medicines. Wilf stops to urinate against a wall and I hear Joy's voice raised in her usual complaint, 'Get on, you dirty old sod you.' Nobody reprimands her for talking that way (to a man twice decorated).

The lies you have to tell to get the medicine into them! We convince Jake it's whisky and he knocks the Largactil back in one swinging movement. 'Cheers!' we say. He raises his glass in salute before shuffling off. Robert sits opposite the medicine trolley on a vinyl-covered chair. I give him the thick orange Brufen liquid with the Largactil mixed in it. He takes it and looks at it appreciatively. 'By God,' he exclaims, 'I bet that puts a gloss on your muck!' Paul and I can't help laughing.

Bob Bates joins in, though he doesn't know what he's laughing at. While he's still affable we try him with his medication. 'Bob, here's some medicine the doctor wants you to take for your chest.' Which is another lie. He takes it and looks at it doubtfully, then wanders off, still holding the medicine pot full of Largactil. 'Come on, Bob, drink up,' I coax him, following the trail of sticky syrup he's slopping on to the floor. 'But you see . . .' Bob starts to explain to me and then forgets what he has been going to say. The medicine pot slips forward in his hand and half the dose slops out on to his trousers. I grab for the pot. He misinterprets my actions. 'Hey, leave me alone,' he warns. I try

47

again. 'Will you drink your medicine please, Bob?' He is already wandering away as I talk to him. Paul shuts the trolley lid and comes towards us. He tries persuasion. It fails and we try to take the medicine left in the pot away from him. 'Come on,' Bob says. 'Stop that now.' He fights to hold on to the pot and the rest of the contents go over my white coat.

We move on to the next patient on our list. Check. Double check. Medicine. Dose. Patient. Time. Route. Little Jimmy's eyes are sticky with infection. Paul tries to get the drops in but Little Jimmy holds his hands away and keeps his eyes tight shut. Together, Paul forcing his eyes open, we get the ointment in. Little Jimmy is upset and chases us back to the trolley waving his fist. So it continues. And now there's a throng round the trolley. Wilf has hold of one end of it and is resolutely trying to push it off down the ward. Further down the ward is the sound of raised voices. I look round in time to see Big Harry and Bob squaring up to one another in a ruck around the doorway. I fly down the ward and Bob only gets one punch in before I catch him and break it up.

Davina stalls Ron's daughter until Lynne comes back to lead her through this throng into the dormitory. Increasingly hysterical sobs and cries drift back to the rest of us. Lynne is having a rough morning. As the hysterics increase we hear the rattle of the porter's mortuary box, a metal coffin on wheels, coming through the service doors at the back. 'Jesus,' says Maisie, scooting off to intercept them and avoid a tricky situation. In the end it takes Lynne and Davina to get Ron's daughter away from her dad. I go and re-wrap the body when she's out of the way. The porters come and watch me through an unclosable gap in the curtains. One of them knew Ron from playing bowls with him. Two of them pick him gently up off the bed and place him carefully in the metal coffin.

We trundle him out the back doors and lift the box into the back of the old hospital ambulance. It is a short, wheel-slipping ride to the mortuary, where the snow is drifting against the door. Bodies in drawers. Ron joins them and I have to sign him in. I cock it up and sign myself in by mistake, much to the amusement of the porters, who threaten to stick me in a drawer and leave me there.

Back on the ward the daughter has departed and a doctor has arrived. He doesn't know the individual patients or how to deal with them, so Lynne has to leave what she is doing to help him. Paul and Davina have started the baths. The doctor checks Blind Tommy's blackened eye. Its OK. 'Got a Woodbine?' asks Tommy. 'After,' Lynne tells him, 'when the doctor's finished.' She turns to me: 'Will you put all Ron's bits and pieces ready for his daughter to pick up? And make a note in the property book of what there is. She doesn't want his clothes, so keep them separate and we can get them marked up for the ward's use.'

I empty the locker, then put all his personal effects into a separate bag. An old electric razor, a watch, two pairs of glasses, a spare set of teeth, a small hand mirror, a St Christopher medal and his pipe and tobacco pouch. His toiletries also go in. On the locker are the Christmas cards he's received. I don't know whether to put them in or not. There's a big musical one at the back and I open it up. A squashed turd adheres to the inside, where some old gent has considerately placed it; through it 'Jingle Bells' drifts faintly to my ears. 'And a Merry Christmas to you too,' I think, slinging all the cards in the bin and finishing off my list.

Wally lies in bed. Paul sits on the edge of it, out of reach of Wally's fists. 'Wally lad, we're only going to give you a nice bath,' Paul explains patiently. Wally fixes him with a reddened eye. 'Go away,' he shouts emphatically. I fetch the commode. Wally is soaking wet. We pull him to an upright position and he spits from the depths of his bronchitic lungs straight into Paul's face. Paul lets go with a sound of disgust and lifts his arm to wipe his face. 'You dirty get!' he exclaims, momentarily losing his composure. Wally takes the opportunity to punch me in the ear before I can grab his free hand. The ear soon warms up nicely. He spits at me. Paul rejoins the battle and gets dragged on to the soaking bedding. Eventually we get a good grip and lift Wally on to the commode, dragging it backwards up the dormitory so he can't gob on us.

In the bathroom Davina perspires freely over a recumbent Rupert. The bath in which he sits is full of scummy water on which float thousands of little black hairs, from where the razor has been sluiced in the tub while shaving him. The floor is wet, Rupert is heavy. Paul helps Davina lift Rupert out on to a chair on which I put a towel. They struggle and I grab his legs. Together we manhandle him on to the chair, accidentally giving his balls a good crack on the side of the bath in the process. He sits in the chair, slumped over from his stroke, wet hair awry, bleary-eyed, complaining.

We turn again to Wally. He glares balefully at us. The bathroom is full of steam. Two electric fires glow above the door to keep the old men warm, but it means Paul and I need to strip off our white coats or expire with the heat. 'Get a load of them bodies,' Davina says, stopping off from drying Rupert's balls to take the piss out of us in her good-natured way. 'It's not right,' shouts Wally between gobs as we bath him. 'It's not right.' He's right. It isn't.

Rupert says in his la-de-dah fashion, 'I think I need to move my bowels.' I give Davina a hand to lift him on to the commode. 'Were you here when his family bought him that electric wheel-chair?' Davina asks. 'Before my time,' I tell her. 'You really missed something there,' she continues. 'It was like the St Valentine's Day Massacre. They put him in it at one end of the ward and he went in a straight line down to the other end. He hadn't got a bloody clue how to control it. There were old men lying everywhere, in heaps they were, clutching on to Zimmer frames, wrestling with each other, throwing punches – they never knew what hit them. That was his first and last trip. We had to ban him.' I smile at the story but would have enjoyed it better if Rupert hadn't been sitting right beside us. I don't like talking about any patient in front of them, even those starting to dement.

Wally is quickly dried and dressed. I cut his toe nails, tough as rhino horn, and clean between his toes with a cotton bud. Wally repeatedly clatters on my back with his fist in protest at my attentions. I'm jammed on my knees in the bathroom between Wally's fists and Rupert's arse. 'Will you bloody well leave me alone,' drifts up the ward from another dissatisfied customer as Paul and Davina get Hugh out of bed.

It doesn't take a moment to rinse out Wally's bath and refill it with clean water and bubble bath, a few minutes longer to tidy up the bathtime detritus. It's not taken long to bath Wally but the little sod's hit me everywhere between the nose and the knees and I'm probably wetter than he is. Hugh walks in, broad-shouldered beneath his only clothing, a pyjama top that exposes the knotted varicosities of his legs and feet. Rupert tells us he has finished. Paul and I stand him up while Davina wipes him. 'Hugh,' Davina shouts, but it's too late. Hugh is happily peeing in the rapidly filling bath. We laugh long and loudly as Hugh, totally unperturbed, continues effortlessly to help fill up the bath, looking at us with a slight disdain on his Butch the bulldog face. Even Rupert grins.

At last it's time for our official tea-break but, unofficially, we all have it together on the ward – we would never get the work finished otherwise. We draw a circle of chairs up with a coffee table in the middle. When everything is ready we take the tray of tea, coffee and toast down to the alcove, draw the chairs tightly round the table and eat under siege conditions. The talk is all of Christmas and the weather. The old men surround us like flies. All they know is we have food and drink and they can't remember having either. Wilf tries to force his way between two chairs and Lynne and I hold him back while still trying to eat and drink ourselves. Wilf looks disgustedly at us. Davina hasn't come yet and several of them try to get into her chair. I need the tea and toast to keep going but there's no enjoyment or relaxation to eating under such conditions.

Davina arrives, still sweating, and we give her some toast and tea off our tray for Hugh so that she doesn't have to go and make him some more. 'I thought you were coming back to help me out the bath with him?' she accuses Paul and me in a bantering fashion. 'I forgot all about it,' Paul laughs guiltily. 'Surely you could manage Hugh on your own?' says Maisie, who's recovered her usual good spirits. 'You've humped bigger men than that in your time.' Davina sticks her tongue out. Jake comes across and

51

holds out his hand to me. We shake. 'What about the stuff for McBacon and eggs?' he queries. I smile reassuringly. 'Leave it with me, Jake. I'll see to it.' He nods and wanders off.

'Your hair's looking a bit damp, Buster,' says Maisie with a twinkle in her eye. I didn't really think I'd be able to keep it quiet. 'Leave the lad alone,' laughs Paul. 'He's had a nasty shock.' 'Oh I wouldnae dream of saying anything,' protests Maisie. Silence falls for a minute as toast and tea and nicotine are consumed. Then Maisie strikes. 'Hey shithead,' she says, 'pass us another slice of toast.' And around the table everybody folds. Crumpled into laughter. Nobody mentions Ron.

Ten-thirty. A distant rumble and the porters, with the help of some strong young patients, are bringing in the laundry. Tub upon tub passes in front of my glazing eyes. 'How you doing, mate?' Brian's overzealous slap on my back nearly makes me jump out of my skin. We've known each other right from my first ward and that's why I'm wary of him. He's a big paranoid schizophrenic, weighing in at just over 20 stone last time I had to put him on the scales, with a record of rapid mood changes and some considerable violence. 'Hello, Brian. How's things?' I ask. He smiles at me but there's no warmth at all. The eyes are cold and suspicious chips glinting out of a pallid, overweight face. Down the other end of the ward Maisie and Paul share a joke. 'Who the fuck are they laughing at?' Brian demands suspiciously. 'Erh, Paul's just telling her a joke,' I say, trying to smooth things over. 'What fucking joke?' Brian demands, looking at me. I think desperately for a joke to tell him and recall one presently doing the hospital circuit. 'What's the three biggest lies ever told?' I stutter. 'Don't know,' says Brian, relaxing slightly. 'This cheque won't bounce; of course I'm not married; I promise not to come in your mouth.' He doesn't laugh out loud but he does smile. 'That's a good one. Got any more?' I tell him a couple more and we make some small talk. Then the artificial smile switches off, leaving a dead face, as Brian grabs his tub and pushes it effortlessly away.

We start again, feeling like we've never stopped. Little Jimmy is wandering down towards the toilets holding his trousers.

'Jimmy, go away,' says Lynne brusquely. 'You've only just been.' 'Hey, hey, hey, hey, Jesus Christ Almighty,' says Jimmy and tries to push past her. We forcibly turn him round and send him packing. 'Fuck, fuck, fuck, fuck,' he hurls over his shoulder at us. The telephone rings as Maisie and I spot another pool of urine. We toss for it and she goes for the bucket. The catering manager is giving me a bollocking on the phone. 'You know the menus have to be in by today at the latest, we're very busy up here you know.' I bite my tongue, apologize, and promise to get the menus up that morning. Before I can get out of the office the phone rings again. This time it's the wife of one of our patients who is on shared care. At the moment he's home for the Christmas holiday. She's telling me she's having some problems but she needn't bother, I can hear him screaming in the background. I fetch Lynne.

Maisie reappears, without the bucket but with a complete set of clean clothes for Wilf and, wrapped in a paper towel, a turd she's found on the way. She nonchalantly chucks the turd down the toilet. 'See if you can find us a pair of size-eight slippers, Buster,' she requests. 'He's crapped all over his others.' I scour the ward and eventually steal a spare pair out of Edwin's locker. The end three beds in the ward are piled high with laundry waiting to be packed away. You wouldn't believe there were that many vests and underpants in the world. The dormitory is kept locked during the day and Robert tries to force past me to go to bed when I unlock it on the way back. It takes me five minutes to convince him it isn't time for bed yet. 'Right-ho, champion,' he eventually concedes with a cheerful smile and wanders back to his chair. Maisie says, 'You took your time, didn't you?' I nearly rise to the bait. Then see her laughing eyes. There's no such thing as doing one thing at a time in this Maddy House and she knows it.

Now, for a brief moment, I have nothing I need to do immediately. Looking around, from my perch on the arm of Blind Tommy's chair, I can see the old men dotted about, some sitting in chairs, one or two talking gibberish to each other, and quite a few in a large group wandering up and down the ward.

The big gang walk past me. They look as if they are going to a football match or even to work, except that one of them is wearing pyjama bottoms. When they reach the door at the end of the ward they all pile up. Those at the front rattle the door handle and bang on the windows. Those at the back push and jostle into them from behind. The front ones turn to come back and there's a mêlée for several minutes. This time nobody falls and there are no fights. They form up again and start back towards me.

Blind Tommy says, 'Got a Woodbine?' He hasn't had his fag yet. Guilty as hell I go and break out a new packet and give one to all those old smokers who still know what a fag is. A couple need watching or they'll set themselves on fire. Jake takes one. His chest rattles and wheezes with the effort of puffing the fag but he looks settled and content for the first time that day. I struggle between feelings of guilt at letting an old bronchitic in his condition smoke and feelings of relief that he is still able to get some brief pleasure out of life.

I knew it couldn't last. Lynne sends me up to the Pharmacy to get some antibiotics that we need for Jake's chest infection. I didn't even know he had one! Better not tell her I've just been and given him a fag. 'Get us twenty Regal while you're out, pet,' she tells me. Outside Pharmacy a young drug addict I know from Acutes waits for his methadone prescription, boasting he makes twice what I earn selling off his surplus to other addicts.

At the shop Martha grabs me from behind. She's been here a lifetime for getting pregnant once. Admitted in the days when such a condition, in an unmarried woman, was considered evidence of a moral state necessitating the protection of in-patient care. Or, more honestly, to hide the shame of the family in a Christian society. We have come that far at least. Promiscuity and immorality are specifically excluded from the 1983 Mental Health Act. Not that it helps Martha much. After a lifetime of being protected in the institution she is no longer sane herself. We have a little dance and the shop staff applaud. I wonder, as we waltz around the grubby floor, whatever became of her baby?

I pick up the wage slips for the ward and take them back with me, opening mine on the way. £291.61 net. In with the pay slip is a little note from the Finance Department saying that in this year of 1984 the 95-pence Christmas bonus will not be paid owing to the financial situation.

Back on the ward, Robert is busy moving furniture. He pulls a chair up to a blank wall, sits down with his feet stretched out and rubs his hands together in front of him, holding them out to the fire he can see but we can't. The door-bell rings. A visitor for Little Jimmy. He cries on my arm, walking up the ward, when he sees a face he recognizes from the past, and goes sobbing on her arm into the small room we keep for visitors to sit in. I walk out leaving the door slightly open behind me. Jake shouts across at me from his chair. 'Shut that fucking door, cunt.' I suppress a smile and do as he bids. 'And keep it fucking shut,' he yells after me.

Lynne asks me to take the patients' new clothes, the ones for Christmas Day, which are in a pile in the office, and hang them up in the store-room. I can't help but smile at the stupidity when I do it. Nearly all the clothes are the same. I'm hanging six jumpers of one design, four of another, twelve pairs of trousers that are identical. The whole idea of buying clothes in town is supposed to be to get away from the old days when everybody wore the same hospital issue.

I find a minute to sit with Hugh. He's still functioning reasonably well in the ward environment, so he doesn't get a lot of attention, which is a shame as he likes to chew the fat. He's another bronchitic. Lynne tells me he's got a mouth organ in the office and when I get it out for him he plays quite well, though he has to stop after every few bars to catch his breath. Which is sort of funny but also hurts you to watch. The music brings back memories to him of his wife and he asks if he can write her a letter. I'm so astonished I can't think what to say but I decide to give it a go. Hugh dictates and I write.

When he's finished he signs his own Christian name in a quavering hand. I can't speak and guess I must look as choked as he does, sitting there with his eyes brimming. Nine lines of love prose on lined Woolworth's paper. For the first time that morning

I'm reminded that these aren't just incontinent old patients, they're fellow human beings, somebody's father, grandfather, brother, uncle, friend or husband. With their own memories, thoughts and feelings. I'm ashamed to be part of a society that cannot give them anything better than this. Taking the mouth organ back to the office I find I've left the door unlocked and Jake is peeing in Lynne's mug, the one she bought on holiday, that has her name written on one side of it and a map of Spain on the other.

The trouble with toileting is that it has a knock-on effect. For a start there are four of us taking a patient each towards the toilets. Then the group wandering the ward automatically latches on to the movement and before we know it two thirds of the ward's patients are jammed into the narrow corridor in front of the toilets. We sit Blind Tommy on the pan. 'There's no fucking toilet paper,' he shouts, feeling at the toilet-roll holder, and there isn't. By the time I get back with it there's two other patients standing with the door open, looking at him. Tommy, unaware of their presence, is giving himself a manual evacuation. Big Harry wanders out without having put his penis away. 'Hey, what's this?' says Maisie, pointing at the offending article. 'Get yerself dressed.' Big Harry gives her his big daft smile, not having understood a word she's said. Maisie laughs and flicks his penis back into his underpants. I wonder what Big Harry's done with his pad?

More of the same and then the crowd starts to thin so we get some of the 'heavy' patients down, those that are doubly incontinent and permanently padded. 'We'll just have to leave him in pyjama bottoms,' Lynne instructs fifteen minutes later as we deal with an accident. It's Big Harry again but now he's run out of clean trousers. My fault for not padding him up. There's always a couple of the old men wandering about in pads and pyjama bottoms while fully dressed on top. It's a peculiar sight, especially as the pyjamas usually end a foot above the shoe. But, thinking about it, so do most of the trousers.

When we go out with Big Harry it's to find Blind Tommy standing in the middle of the corridor waiting for someone to take him to wash his hands. He complains bitterly about the other nurses. 'They went and fucking left me,' he yells. Funny, but it's impossible not to like the little bugger, even though he does make a lot of extra work and never says anything nice about anybody.

It's lunchtime so I take Blind Tommy straight from washing his hands into the dining room. Another chaotic rush. Jake wets himself sitting at the table and we leave him like that until he's finished eating. 'Better put him to bed this afternoon,' Lynne instructs. 'I think he's getting worse.' Robert pushes up the window, which only opens about eight inches, and gets one leg through. 'I've got to get home to feed the cats,' he remonstrates when I pull him back in. 'It's all right,' I lie to him, 'I've already done it.' The afternoon staff come on duty while we're still dishing out lunch and the sight of them trailing down the ward cheers us up no end.

After lunch Davina and I start on the laundry. Although everything has been washed it is nearly all stained from faeces or urine or tea or Horlicks or whatever else has been spilled down it. The vests are all distorted and shrunk with repeated washings and most of the pyjamas have no buttons left on them. A lot of them are badly ripped and Davina throws some of them out because it's the only way to stop the laundry sending them back to us. It scares me to think I might end up in here one day wearing stuff like this, convicted of the crime of growing old.

It's pleasant to be away from the old men for a while. The dormitory is clean, the sheets are crisp and pleasantly smooth to the touch, and there's nobody to pick up, keep an eye on, clean up or amuse. Not that we slouch. We're a well-oiled machine and the laundry is soon showing signs of our attention. Paul comes through. He's going home early as there is time owing to him. He's jubilant to be off and makes leery eyes to me about Davina behind her back. I laugh and she turns, catches him doing it and chases him up the ward, both of them enjoying it. Our moods are all much lighter now.

Last, the personal laundry. Bags full of trousers, shirts, jumpers and socks. I stick my hand into a sock, to turn it the right way round, and gasp. There's a large lump of faeces at the toe-end, into which I've just stuck three fingers of my right hand! Davina rolls away up the dormitory, laughing hysterically. Walking past her I raise my hand. 'Just going to give my hair a wash,' I joke. What can you say?

When I come back from scrubbing my hand we start to make up the bundles of clothes that the old men will be wearing tomorrow. The better-off, better-cared-for patients subsidize the others, as we borrow from Peter to clothe Paul. The lockers stink of urine.

Towards the end Maisie comes in to help us finish off. It's one o'clock and she's been making the patients' sandwiches ready for the evening meal at five o'clock, leaving them covered by wet paper sheets on a large tray. 'I take it that was just gossip about Rosemary?' I ask, referring back to Joy and Florrie's jibes. 'Could you believe them two!' exclaims Maisie. 'They were lucky not to get the toe of my boot up their arses. Of course it was just gossip. Don't tell me you think she's been nicking stuff as well?' 'Don't be stupid,' I answer, wondering what I have been thinking.

The dormitory door opens as we finish. 'Report,' Lynne says, sticking her head round the door and smiling. We gather for a moment in the gallery as Lynne gets the Kardex from the office. Robert ambles up to Maisie and grabs her by the tits. 'By, they're a good pair and all,' he exclaims, fondling them happily. Maisie laughs too, removing his hands and saying, 'They're a bit better than your wife's, Robert, eh?' Now everybody's laughing and she gives him a hug and a kiss. The first normal contact I've seen today. Davina comes out of the kitchen with a tray of tea and coffee, Lynne comes out of the office with the Kardex and we go for Report.

As we sit locked in our little room the patients come and peer at us through the glass panes in the door. Some smile and wave. Some rattle the door and call out, trying to get in and join us. Occasionally the door-bell rings and Davina or Maisie, left out on the ward, go past to answer it. Once I have to go out to cover while they change Big Harry, who's wet himself and half the length of the corridor. Fag smoke curls up past the tall windows and on towards the ceiling. We all slow down and start to feel the tiredness from the shift. My mind switches to the afternoon ahead and starts planning what's to be done at home.

Lynne tells us to go. We head rapidly for the changing room, laughing and joking, turn the corner at the end of the gallery and there's Big Harry, stinking. We can't leave him! Hospital tradition dictates each shift clears up its own muck. We descend on Big Harry like a plague of locusts and take him to the medi-bath room. He stands between us and home, two of us have a bus to catch; we're not rough but we are in a hurry.

Big Harry is changed in record time and fired out into the corridor. He's still there a minute later when we run past him. I grab my coat and shoes from my locker and go out into the dormitory, so that the girls can get changed. Then Davina and I run off up the corridor for the bus: no time to say goodbyes, even to Jake, who's now in bed and may be dead tomorrow.

At the stop the last of the queue is climbing on to the bus. We shout and they wait for us as we slither across the forecourt. A couple of patients clearing the snow turn to watch. And then we sit together, slowly winding down the few miles into town. Looking at Davina, thinking of the others, feeling myself to have been in the company of heroes.

I let myself into the house, pick up the small pile of cards on the mat and walk through to the kitchen. At least we can call it something now it's got a roof on. The only other things in it are an old sink, held up by water pipes at the back and a lump of wood at the front, and a new 'bottom of the range' cooker, still waiting to be re-fitted. We've been doing up the house for so long I can't remember a time when it did look half normal.

I'm too tired even to slip my coat off, physically and mentally drained. Standing dripping snow in the kitchen waiting for the kettle to boil. There's a smell of new wood from the floorboards laid yesterday. Outside the window is a monumental pile of builders' rubbish. As I stand motionless a small black rabbit hops into sight on top of this pile of bricks and debris. I look at it, first with disbelief, then, when it doesn't go away, with a feeling of absolute horror. Am I hallucinating in my own kitchen? 'No, get a grip,' I tell myself. 'There must be a logical reason why, in the middle of the worst winter for years, there is a baby rabbit hopping about on top of a pile of bricks in a back yard surrounded by high walls to which the only entrance is a locked gate.' I start to get myself under control. Then another bunny hops into view! I'm wiped out. 'Oh God,' I say out loud, feeling panicky, my palms sweating, thinking of the wards, of being a patient there, of other staff who have gone that way before me. How long I stand there I don't know. Seeing rabbits, wishing I wasn't. The key turns in the front door and the builder comes in. I really don't want to ask this question. My mouth is parched but I force myself to speak, my whole life revolving around his answer, 'Can you see anything odd in that back yard?' He looks out. 'Oh aye,' he says. 'Strange, ain't it? I found 'em in the back lane when I was bringing some stuff in. Thought I'd better shove 'em in here until I could think what to do with 'em. Must have escaped from somebody's hutch, I suppose. I see you've got the kettle on.'

Friday 21 December

Little Edna walks bare-footed from her bed as we sip our coffee and wish the day would go away. On this cold morning Edna, wearing only a nightie, moves from foot to foot, struggling to express the thoughts of her eighth decade. We try to get her into a dressing gown and slippers but she resists so strongly that leaving her to calm down seems the best thing to do. Edna chunters on about some man and his trumpet, but none of us listens.

Nikki comes in. 'Hello Edna, did you sleep all right?' she asks, putting her arm protectively around this tiny figure. Edna's eyes start to fill with tears. 'What's up, Edna?' Nikki asks, concerned. 'I'll never sleep in that room again,' Edna says, crying now, 'never!' Nikki's really surprised. 'But Edna, you said how much you liked it in there. What's happened?' Edna speaks between sobs. 'That man's found me again, Sister, he's been playing that trumpet outside my window all night. I haven't slept a wink!' Sam snorts into his coffee and nearly chokes.

We return to our drinks. Edna goes away and then comes back again to stand beside us, worrying me with her bare, cold feet. 'If she gets any smaller,' Sam jokes, 'I'm going to stick her on top of the Christmas tree.' Joan, looking tired after her night on duty, mentions that Edna hasn't slept at all.

We take Report in Sister's office, away from the sharp ears of any early-morning patients who might be wandering the ward. 'I'm afraid you've got a bit of a problem,' Joan tells Nikki. 'George and Ida both died during the night.' 'Both of them?' Nikki answers, really surprised. 'That's a bit of a shock. I mean. I know they've both been on the way out for a while but still, you don't expect it, and not both of them at once.' 'I know,' Joan answers a bit sarcastically, probably with being so tired. 'It's just not on, is it? Anyway,' she continues, 'that's not the problem. The problem is that we can't get rid of the bodies – the ambulance can't get out of the garage because of the snow.' 'Oh no, tell me you're joking,' Nikki pleads. 'It's not that bad,' Joan reassures her, 'The garden squad are going to dig the ambulance out straight after breakfast, so it won't be too long before they come and fetch them.' 'You what?' butts in Sam. 'Have you ever seen the garden squad in action? I've seen more life in a dog's pelt than there is in that bunch. Those bodies will still be here tomorrow if we've got to rely on that shower of tossers.' 'Where have you put them?' Nikki asks the question I've been thinking. 'Well, we managed to get Ida in the sluice,' Joan tells her. Then she screws her face up apologetically. 'But I'm afraid George is in the games room.' It starts to get hard to keep a straight face. 'Oh terrific,' says Sam. 'I'll get some of the others to nip in and have a game of pool with him while he's waiting.' Sniggers break out which Nikki quells with difficulty. In the middle of this, Liam, our SEN, arrives covered in snow and carrying a shovel which he's obviously had to use to get here. 'Forget the ambulance,' Sam quips. 'Just give 'em to Liam and he'll nip outside and bury 'em for us.' Liam, who hasn't a clue what's going on, looks bemusedly about him as we dissolve into laughter.

After Report I go and put the lights on in the male dormitory and start to rouse the patients. It's not half past seven yet but breakfast is at eight and that dictates an early start. From a distance the smile fools me, but when I get closer to Brian I see it's as bloodless and humourless as that of a corpse. When he sees me heading towards him he gets up out of bed and deliberately walks away. He's so rigid he looks like he's bolted together and gives the impression of something very big and very dangerous wrapped in bands of slowly fraying steel. I'm not surprised by the change in him since yesterday, which is definitely for the worse, and I don't try and stop him! He certainly doesn't look like he wants to hear any more of my jokes. It strikes me he wasn't here for my night shift on Tuesday but I suppose he was just home on leave, probably for a long weekend. 'Pity he's not home on leave today,' I think to myself, having had dealings with Brian in the past.

Walter pretends to be asleep on my first pass. When I come back he lies there, his face miserable on the pillow. Getting his clothes out of the locker and putting them on the bed is supposed to be my only concession to helping him dress, though I stay on to advise and chivvy him along. Wearily Walter goes through the motions. He tugs and pulls and struggles. 'I'm no good you know,' he tells me. 'I smell, I'm dirty. It's my bowels, they're blocked up solid; it makes me stink.' I try to reassure him but he doesn't want to know. At one point, sitting on the edge of the bed, he tries to put a sock on his remaining foot and overbalances backwards where he lies, looking up at me, a mute appeal for help on his face. This is really hard to do.

With the artificial leg and the trousers, he breaks me down. It's just impossible to watch such pathetic struggling and not get exasperated with him at the slowness of it all. All he has managed is to get the sock over the stump, though not before complaining that the stump was sore and chafed, which, of course, it wasn't. Just another attempt to get out of wearing the artificial leg. He would rather have a day in a wheelchair. I dress the artificial limb with one leg from a pair of trousers. The leg weighs a ton and feels big and cumbersome and solid. Walter does his famous bemused look when my help stops. With my encouragement he gets the stump into the leg but then fumbles at the strapping for so long I can't stand it any more and do it up for him. 'You don't like helping me, do you?' he queries. 'I don't blame you, not the way I smell. It's that bad, people complain to Sister about it. They're trying to get me put into isolation. I think they're right.'

Liam sticks his head through the curtains. He has the florid rounded features and gingery brown hair of an Irish horse-trainer. 'Walter,' he says gently, 'don't forget you are having ECT today. Have nothing to eat or drink this morning, please.' For the first time this morning I see a spark of life in Walter's eyes, a momentary thing which is immediately gone and leaves me wondering if it was ever really there. Walter still has a long way to go, starting with a trip to the washroom which he doesn't want to make. My instinct is to carry his gear down for him, as with the leg and the crutches to contend with, it hardly seems fair to make him manage his toiletries and towel as well. That, however, will do him no good at all, so I hold myself in check and make him manage on his own. As he will have to do at home.

Liam helps me make the beds. He tells me he was up at five this morning to make sure he got here for seven. Not that he lives far away but his house is half a mile off the main road and at the moment he has to dig himself out every morning. As an SEN Liam would actually be better off on the dole. But here he is. Never a groan about the patients; never a moan about the pittance of a wage; no jealousy for those less able than him, who get more money and status for doing the job worse than he does just because they're Registered; always time to stop and talk; unflappable in a crisis. How he does it is a mystery to me.

When Walter comes back we praise him up to the eyeballs. It's all part of the treatment. Make him do something he can achieve and reward him well for any success, no matter how small. 'You don't have to lie to me,' Walter replies. 'I come from a long line of villains and murderers and they all stank.'

The others have been getting on faster than me, most of the patients being less physically dependent than Walter, and the boilers are bouncing away in the kitchen when I eventually get there. The domestic hasn't made it through the snow to work so Nikki has organized the ward kitchen. A great pile of freshly made toast sits temptingly on a plate, and a half-slice slips into my unresisting hand. It tastes good and buttery and gives me a little boost, though it would cost me my job if I was discovered eating hospital food. I fill the tea-pots.

Breakfast is always the first major battle of the day. There have been minor skirmishes up and down the ward for the last hour but now the manipulators manipulate, the anorexics cheat, the depressed simply refuse, the confused mess it all up and the whole lot seem to put on a show, one for the other, to prove they are ill.

Edna starts before we even get anybody sat down. She refuses to go into breakfast at all and at her age nobody is going to fight with her over a piece of toast and a cup of tea. Having originally come in for assessment, following her strange behaviour at home, it has now been decided that she is in fact dementing. She is waiting for a bed on geriatrics – waiting, that is, for someone to die, so she can take her place in death's constantly moving queue.

Young Emma Jane comes in for the worst, the most shaming, part of her day. To eat with people, some of whom she's treated here as a doctor, others who know what she does from the grapevine and stop eating to stare at her. She sits with her head bowed and pecks at her food, conversing with no one, shutting herself off from the reality of her situation. She's no longer hypomanic and the danger now is that she appears to be swinging back into a depression. I hope that she can't remember her streak down the corridor on Tuesday night.

Gloria, our overweight, domineering staff nurse, comes in with Dorothy who is causing her some problems. Dorothy, a grey-haired, varicose-veined butcher's wife, is extremely psychotic at the moment, her behaviour eccentric due to her deluded thinking. She is covered in bruises from throwing herself out of bed and on to the floor. Her medication makes her salivate excessively so that her mouth is always dirty and sticky. Dorothy talks constantly, responding to the voices she hears. We try to keep her in just her dressing gown and slippers, so that it is harder for her to wander away from the ward without being spotted, but she is constantly trying to dress and undress herself in a variety of clothes so that she can go home. Gloria sits her down and stands next to her so that she doesn't get up and rush off. It is very difficult to get her to eat because she is so excited by the ongoing voices in her mind, to which she is constantly respond-ing, that she cannot concentrate long enough to get the food down. She is on constant observation for her own safety.

Carol, an attractive young mother with a bad case of puerperal psychosis, arrives with the baby in a pushchair. It really is a pretty child but Carol is red-eyed and puffy-faced from crying. Voices tell her to kill the baby, torment her to strangle it. She sobs to Nikki, 'I love my baby, I love him, oh please don't let me hurt him.' She cannot understand what is happening to her. It is tearing her in two. Dorothy wants to get up and give the baby some bacon. Gloria shoves her back down in the chair with a stern, 'Behave.' It is too much for Carol who retreats quickly from the room without eating anything. Nikki goes after her with a cup of tea and some toast.

I go off for my own breakfast in the staff dining room. Sally, a fellow student but working on a different ward, comes in and sits down beside me. She needs to talk. 'It was my bad luck to find him, I can't tell you how it felt. At first it looked just like somebody hiding behind the toilet door but somehow I knew it wasn't. When I opened it he came swinging out towards me.' Her eyes are staring straight ahead as she tries to explain it. 'He'd used his belt, it didn't look strong enough to hold a man up, but there he was, the eyes popping out of the head, stone dead.' She pauses, as if she has forgotten all about my presence, and drinks some tea. Twenty-one years old, somebody's daughter, and having to deal with this horror. 'I tried to lift him, to get him down, but he was too heavy for me. All the time I was shouting and shouting for help. Sister came, though it seemed to take ages for her to get there, and we got him down between us. Sister says, "You'll have to go through the motions, try and resuscitate him while I phone for the doctor. It's to cover ourselves." I couldn't believe what she was saying. It nearly made me sick to do it.' An intimate vision of her warm pink lips on his cold blue mouth comes to me.

It's a week since the man has hung himself. She needs to talk about it still because nobody has given her any help to deal with it, to take it away from her. They asked her what happened, she wrote it all down, and that was that. Nobody came back to see how it had affected her. As if she were a robot or something that can go round kissing dead men without taking any harm from it. 'Anyway, I've applied for a job in town, working in an office, anything but this, this . . .' She finishes, lost for words now, smiles, takes up her cup and leaves to wash it out. Her eyes big and moist.

Returning from breakfast I apprehend Edna wandering

towards the exit from the building. She can't tell me where she wants to go but she certainly wants to get there badly. Again and again she wanders off the ward in just her dress and cardigan. It's freezing outside, though it's stopped snowing, and every time somebody goes to bring her back she gets more and more agitated. Gloria is reprimanded in the car park by a doctor as she drags Edna back on to the ward for the umpteenth time. 'If any doctor told me off I'd soon tell him where to stuff it,' remarks Sam. 'Sodding cheek, they've nowt to do with us.' I try to get Edna to sit quietly in the sitting room but she pushes up out of the chair repeatedly. Every time she struggles she gets worse. Mary Chambers surprises me by offering to look after Edna and I happily leave her to it.

Gloria is rounding up the patients for Occupational Therapy. She reminds me of a circus ringmaster as she charges about trying to get them all together. Most of them are trying to get out of doing it. 'If I have to make one more bloody paper chain I'll scream,' Mary Chambers complains. 'You just don't know what it's like. Cutting up last year's Christmas cards to make gift tags; baking mince pies – my God, I must have made enough mince pies in the last couple of weeks to keep this bloody place supplied for the next ten years; singing carols until you're sick of the sound of them; some idiot asking you "What do you normally do at Christmas, Mary?" Oh no, I can't stand another day up there. Anyway, Buster asked me to look after Edna.' Gloria gives me a withering look and I understand why Mary offered to help with Edna, trying to manipulate her way out of Occupational Therapy.

Liam and I go and get the ECT patients ready. Electro-Convulsive Therapy, that is. But there's no need to call it that in here. They all know exactly what ECT stands for! Mabel and Walter are the only two from this ward today. They've both had it before; Mabel is an old hand. She chunters on as usual about being no good. Her notes are a great thick wedge of misery labelled Volume Three. Walter, being recently depressed, has a slim, neat file.

We walk slowly off down the corridor, myself abreast of Walter, his disability determining our pace, Mabel and Liam following. Walter asks me, 'Does it do any good, do you think?' I try and tell the truth but there is no one truth to that question. 'It seems to depend very much on the individual,' I tell him. 'How about me, do you think?' he queries. 'Will it do me any good?' Walter doesn't like the treatment. He's had four now and knows the after-effects of splitting headaches and nausea. What he's really asking me is does he really have to go through with this again? 'Don't you want the treatment?' I ask gently, responding to the question behind the question. We are still moving at a snail's pace towards the ECT suite. He can't answer and just chews his lip nervously. 'They can't make you have it you know,' I remind him. 'You do have to consent.' But, as reluctant as Walter is to have any more ECT, he's even more reluctant to come into conflict with the consultant over refusing treatment. 'I stink,' he says.

There are three other patients already waiting in the room, all middle-aged to elderly. Maisie, who is on one of the other acute wards, is sitting talking to them. They have had their teeth and glasses removed in preparation for the treatment. Rings have been either taken off or taped over, watches and valuables removed and put in a bag for safe-keeping. The sunken cheeks, marked noses and squinting eyes reveal all. Mabel and Walter are also divested of their teeth. It's not possible to do it privately, no provision has been made for that in this brand-new suite of rooms. The others watch as I hand them a bag each and they slide out their false teeth and drop them in. Walter's need cleaning, I notice. Their names are written on the bags which are put into a locked drawer.

It seems unnecessary to subject them to this process in full view of everybody else, especially when some of them will be sitting here waiting for an hour or more. An hour without teeth, no wonder they don't talk much; an hour without glasses, no wonder they don't attempt to read the out-of-date magazines.

'Buster, will you wait out here? You other two come with me.' That's the ECT nurse speaking. Liam goes to supervise the recovery room, Maisie to help with the ECT. Before she goes she asks me, 'Can I have a word with you later on?' 'Are you playing in the match?' I ask her. She nods. 'How about afterwards?' I suggest. 'Yeah, OK, that'll do fine.' The room goes quiet, apprehensive. I am supposed to attend to the mental and emotional strain these five people are experiencing and keep them calm. Three of them I've never seen before today. How do you reassure a perfect stranger that a treatment involving the shocking of the brain to induce a fit and the administration of a general anaesthetic will do them no harm? Every year people die having this done! I sit there and wonder what Maisie wants.

'Walter, will you come in now please?' Maisie smiles reassuringly and holds the door open as Walter shuffles slowly through into the adjoining room. We can hear the faint muttering of low-pitched voices and everybody strains to catch the words. After ten minutes or so a loud hum is heard. It lasts several seconds. Everybody tenses, relaxing only when the hum ends. It's like sitting in a dentist's waiting room and hearing his drill whining away. But worse. A short while later Maisie comes out for the next customer.

Mabel is sitting on my right. As the proceedings drag on she gets more and more impatient, tensing up each time that hum vibrates through the room. 'How much longer are they going to be, son? I'm fed up with all this.' She is plucking nervously at her dress. 'Can I have a fag, eh? One fag won't do us any harm, will it?' Part of me wonders why every nurse–patient communication seems to be in the form of questions and answers. 'I wouldn't if I was you, Mabel, not if you're about to have an anaesthetic; besides, your bag's locked away.' She looks at me but says nothing for a minute. 'Oh aye, I've had enough of this.' She is on her feet and heading for the door. 'Mabel, come on now. What are you doing?' My hand is on the door handle so she can't bolt out. 'Let me out that door. I'm off. I've had enough of this carry-on.' 'I can't stop you going, Mabel, if that's what you want' – though I'm doing just that – 'but think about it for a minute, eh? What good is it going to do you bolting off up the corridor? That isn't going to make you feel any better, is it?' She's already going off the idea. 'You lot, you're all the bloody same,' she says quietly.

Mabel's the last patient to go in so I go through with her. Inside the door, through which everybody has gone, is a small room containing all the paraphernalia of ECT. There's a trolley-bed in the middle, an oxygen cylinder with a black ambubag for resuscitation, the ECT box, out of which sprout a few black leads. Around the walls are drug cabinets, sinks, and various other units such as you'd find in any household kitchen. At the far end of the room are some double doors. 'Take your shoes off please, Mabel,' requests the ECT nurse. And when this is done: 'Right, just get on the couch for me and lie flat on your back, please.' I wonder if she had to ask Walter to take his leg off. Mabel suddenly asks, 'What have I got to have this for? I don't want this.' Her voice rises as the speaks. The anaesthetist looks up from his preparations, wondering whether to go on, perhaps. The ECT nurse says, 'Come on, Mabel, let's get it over and done with and then you can have a nice cup of tea.' 'I can have a nice cup of tea without getting bloody zapped first,' Mabel shouts. The doctor adds his voice. He's an Indian, been here for years but still speaks poor English. To compensate he shouts. 'Mabel, don't waste our time. Why did you sign consent form? What will Dr Jones say?' Always that reference back to the consultant when a patient gets sticky. Mabel crumbles at the prospect of facing the wrath of a minor god. It was a token gesture anyway. Nobody who has signed a consent form gets this far and then backs out – not in my experience.

Mabel gets on the bed and lies down. There's six of us standing around her plus the paraphernalia of treatment. I wonder how it looks to her down there. The anaesthetist goes about his business. 'All right, Mabel, just a little prick in the back of the hand.' He slides the butterfly needle into the vein and tapes it down. First the atropine, to dry up the secretions, then the Pentothal, the general anaesthetic of choice. 'OK, you are going to sleep now, Mabel. Count after me one, two . . .' Mabel doesn't make it to five. Working quickly, deftly, the anaesthetist pulls off the Pentothal syringe and fits on the Scoline, the muscle relaxant, to stop her breaking her back or legs when she convulses. The doctor meanwhile is checking the ECT box. He checks the duration and strength of the current-setting, that the pads which will fit against Mabel's temples are moist so that she gets a good contact, that the current is flowing. The anaesthetist continues working. The ambubag mask goes over Mabel's face and he ventilates her with the mixture. When her colour is right he steps back, and the ECT nurse slips a gag between Mabel's remaining teeth. It is shaped like a horseshoe with a handle on the curved end, and is made of thick rubber to stop her biting through it. She has some trouble getting this in. The doctor moves forward. We grip Mabel's arms. Sombody's forearm goes under her chin. The rest of us lean forward to hold down the length of her body. I'm directly opposite Maisie. The doctor places the pads against her temples and presses the buttons. That hum again. But this time much louder and more intense without the wall to interfere. It reminds me of slaughtering time at the abattoir.

For the four seconds it lasts the shock seems to be trying to stretch Mabel. Her head goes back with a jerk, as if in extreme pain, the feet stretch away from the body towards the end of the couch, the toes pointing away even further. Unconscious or not there is an agony in the screwed-up eyes which makes me uncomfortable to be a part of this. Maisie and I lean forward with our faces inches apart. Both of us hating this. And then the humming stops.

The fit seems to start at the top of her body and in a jerking restless rush takes hold of the length of her, right down to the feet. For maybe half a minute we hold on tightly as she rushes through our hands in a convulsion, then, as if someone had thrown another switch, it is past and the worst of her discomfiture is over.

The anaesthetist replaces the doctor at her head. The gag is removed to be replaced by the airway which is inserted into the mouth, neatly turned and slid down the throat. The ambubag ventilates Mabel again. The first time it's removed Mabel isn't breathing. Or the second time. The anaesthetist's eyes check the location of the emergency drugs and the defibrillator. The doctor hears the growing silence and turns away from Mabel's file to look. The mask stays on longer this time. Some small tension builds in the room. When the mask comes off for the third time Mabel breathes herself. The airway is left in place and we roll her over on to her left-hand side and cover her with a blanket; then she is pushed through the double door and into the recovery room.

Walter is just staggering out the other end as we go in. He is being helped by Liam. The other patients are still on their couches, feet to the wall, heads to the centre of the room, for our easy access in cases of emergency. Mabel joins them. The anaesthetist has a word with Liam when he comes back in and they go to look at Mabel. I help to get the others ready. One old lady grips her airway firmly between her gums, worrying and biting at it. 'Good job I'm not a Freudian,' I joke to Maisie. She doesn't understand, then does, and punches me on the arm. 'You dirty auld bugger,' she laughs.

We put the gags and airways in mild disinfectant and restore the teeth, watches and shoes to their owners. None of them wants to get up and we have to cajole them to their feet. As they stagger through for a cup of tea and a slice of toast they look like those pictures of survivors you see on the TV news. Walter has a lovely flush, from the atropine, I guess, and is lobster-red. Only Mabel has still to come round. She starts coughing weakly but cannot clear her throat. Liam gets the suction machine going and does it for her. It sounds like a child emptying the dregs from a can of Coke through a straw.

Mabel eventually joins the rest for a cup of tea. I don't know what's happened to her hair but it's sticking straight out, making her look like some sort of cartoon character. She sits with the patients at one table, the staff sit at another. Most of the patients look dazed, stupid. We chat and laugh, enjoying our unofficial tea-break. They say nothing. The ECT nurse comes through and makes the doctors a drink. Walter's sick. I clean it up and then go back to my tea. It's not a thing that bothers me any more. What bothers me are the five pairs of haunted bloodshot eyes that watch me doing it. I take Mabel and Walter back to the ward. When Sam sees Mabel's hair he jokes, 'You're not supposed to plug 'em into the mains you know, Buster.' I put them both on their separate beds and cover them with a blanket while they recover. Sam tells me the two bodies have been shifted. 'Pity, eh Buster?' he adds. 'I think even you might have won a game of pool against him in the games room.'

The day is starting to quicken. Edna is still trying to leave and I have a spell of looking after her. It seems now that Edna wants to know where Violet is. Whoever she might be. She has three or four questions about Violet of which one will surface and be asked repeatedly. Nobody can stand it for long. When the staff aren't there the other patients abuse her because she pesters them and she is old and frail.

Holding down the diminutive Edna with one hand, I spend a long time going over her problems. She agrees, yes, her memory isn't what it used to be: 'Where's Violet, please?' She listens in an agitated fashion to what I have to say, pushing against me all the time. Nobody has ever shown me how to talk to a lady like this, with no memory. In the end I write out a list answering all four of her questions about Violet and tuck it in her handbag. Now, whenever she wants to know the answer to them, all she has to do is look. The catch has hardly shut on her bag when she asks, 'Where's Violet please?' I refer her to the list. 'What list?' she asks. I get the list out for her. 'Oh yes, now I remember.' Edna asks me all the questions on the list this time. Again. And again. My only hope now is to get the list off her before her questions drive me crazy! She is still pushing against my hand and now she won't give the list up. It has become important to her. With some relief I hear an altercation in the corridor and run outside.

Dorothy is staggering about with Sam following her. 'Give us a break, man,' he gasps at me. 'I'm dying for a slash.' The more I follow Dorothy the more agitated she becomes, shouting and swearing at me over her shoulder. A cup of tea comes and she takes a drink. She is so unsteady it seems only a matter of time until the cup will smash on the floor, which it does. All the time I'm talking to Dorothy, trying to get some sort of relationship

73

established. She scuttles off up the ward, unimpressed with my efforts. Her back is half against the wall, her head turned to see if I am still following her around. Heaven knows who she thinks I am. She tries to leave the ward and we have a little wrestling match on the doorstep which is watched with interest by some visitors outside in a car, me in my white coat, Dorothy in the dressing gown with the flowers on it. Dorothy heaps abuse upon my shoulders. 'Leave me alone, you big bully. Go on, piss off. You should be chopped in three.' The latter she tries to achieve by swinging her handbag at me. Fortunately, judging by the bulging size of it, she misses. Now I follow her back down the corridor. 'What are you following me for? Get lost.' She darts into the female toilet. I follow but there's a half-naked young patient in there and I have to leave again. Gloria is passing. 'Get Dorothy out of there for me, will you?' I beseech her. She looks askance but goes and does it. The Dorothy that comes out bears no resemblance to the one that went in. She has been under the shower fully clothed, fallen and bashed her nose which has bled all over her. 'You're supposed to be keeping her on constant observation,' Gloria reprimands me. 'Is that too much to ask?' I sting. She continues, 'Dorothy's daughters are already half convinced that we beat her up because of all her bruises. What they will say to this doesn't bear thinking about!'

Nikki shouts to me from the bottom of the corridor as Gloria stomps off the other way to get Dorothy some dry clothes. '*Heil Hitler*,' I mutter under my breath to her retreating back. 'Buster, come and give us a hand here.' She is trying to get a struggling Edna to the clinical room. Dorothy, of course, is still with me and reprimands us. 'Here, what are you doing to that old lady? Leave her alone.' The four of us, Dorothy fighting on the side of Edna, finally tumble into the clinical room after a long battle up the corridor. Nikki goes to phone the duty doctor. 'You should be ashamed of yourself,' Dorothy says, winding me with a lucky blow from her handbag that catches me in the solar plexus. She's on her way out the door with Edna when Gloria comes back and stops her. I try to smile up at Gloria from my bent-over position near the floor. She shakes her head at me and takes Dorothy away to clean her up. Edna gets an extra dose of promazine and Nikki and I put her to bed. She settles quickly but ten minutes later staggers out into the corridor hardly able to stand. 'Hey, hey, give us the toilet,' she shouts. We fetch a commode to her room and then struggle to get her on it. She has an enormous bowel movement and empties her bladder. We all feel really stupid because now we know why she has been so agitated. But that doesn't help Edna.

Carol is arguing with a re-dressed Dorothy when I come back from emptying the commode. There's no sign of Gloria, who should be looking after her. Dorothy wants to hold the baby, she must hold the baby, it's hers! Sam arrives and we pull Dorothy away to the sitting room and warn her off. She's getting increasingly strange. Sam tells me off for not watching Dorothy properly. I point out I wasn't supposed to be. 'And don't tell tales,' he snaps. Carol is crying again, she has enough problems without this. Sam goes off to see what's to be done about Dorothy. Dr Jones decides to transfer her to the female disturbed ward. It seems like it has been on the cards for a few days but this has put the seal on it. Everybody's a bit touchy about kids, after one was killed here once, many mad moons ago. While Sam's away Dorothy throws a large glass ashtray through the window. Which makes me just about the most popular person in the ward, I don't think!

Nikki sits with Dorothy now, in the corner of the lounge. Dorothy smokes, inhaling deeply, and I admire Nikki's legs from my discreet observation point just outside the door. The ambulance arrives, the beat-up one we use for internal transfers of patients, dead and alive, so Sam and I go in for her. She sees us coming but doesn't move until Sam says, 'Come on, Dorothy,' and starts to pull her up out of the chair, when she starts fighting wildly, stubbing her cigarette out on my hand when I try to restrain her. Once inside the ambulance, though, she calms down and causes us no further trouble. 'Got a fag?' she asks Staff Nurse on the female disturbed ward. We have to walk back through the snow, the driver having gone off for his tea-break and dumped us. It's freezing and my white coat offers little protection. Sam doesn't even have a white coat on.

An old lady of 79 is admitted, much to everyone's surprise. The reason for the surprise is that she was only discharged yesterday to spend Christmas at home. 'Hello, what are you doing back here?' Sam asks. 'Hello, Nurse,' she answers. 'I's been fighting with me cousin, Nurse; she said I was daft, Nurse, and that I should be in the loony bin all the time. That hurt me, Nurse, cos I's not daft, so I hit her and she pulled me hair. But we made it up before the police came and we're friends again now.' 'How old is your cousin,' Sam asks disbelievingly. 'She's 89, Nurse,' answers the old lady. 'Is there any tea going spare?'

Emma Jane looks in at me as she drifts down the corridor to get herself a coffee. Her blue eyes briefly rest on mine. It's obvious she wants to talk. Knowing her as both a patient and a doctor is all rather confusing. I follow her into the kitchen and ask the standard opening question, 'How are you today, Emma Jane?' She gives that wan little smile of the hard-done-by. 'How would you feel locked up in here?' she counters sulkily, her young face registering her disapproval at her situation. I hate to see her like this. We are both in the kitchen, alone. Gloria comes in. 'Dr Jones would like to see you now, Emma Jane.' Then she looks questioningly at me, her gaze saying, 'Don't be so bloody daft.' What's concerning her is that I'm a male nurse and Emma Jane is a young female patient. Emma Jane drifts away up the corridor, misery surrounding her like a cloak. Gloria stops and talks. 'You want to be careful, you know, Buster!' I sigh an 'I know' in agreement because really she is right, but just how do you ever help anybody in this kind of set-up, where you're always looking over your shoulder?

I hit a quiet five minutes. Sitting down with a cup of coffee and a book. Liam is sitting reading the Bible. I try to memorize the side-effects of amitriptyline as, believe it or not, I'm supposed to be able to study in the middle of this lot. Somebody is trying to talk to me, a patient off the 'roundabout' who obviously knows me from previous admissions. I can't remember who she is and pay scant attention until I half-hear her saying, 'Everybody likes you, Buster, because you listen to them.' It makes me feel like an absolute swine and I start running around the ward having intense conversations with anybody who wants to talk to me. Edna's daughter comes up to me in the day room, a bemused expression upon her face. 'She thinks she's naked,' she says, shaking her head. 'She thinks she hasn't got any clothes on.' Then she walks away without waiting for an answer.

It starts off innocuously enough. Just two young male out-patients playing pool in the games room, laughing and joking about. Brian comes storming up to me, fighting a battle for control of himself. 'Get them two bastards out of here,' he shouts. 'Get them out before I fucking kill them.' The two youths are reluctant to leave the pool table they've only just been able to get on, until Brian appears in the doorway. 'I told you to get them two bastards out,' he roars. 'Come on,' I tell them, acting calm, feeling queasy with the violence to come. They follow like shadows.

My mind is whizzing round. 'What's Brian doing while I'm shepherding these two away?' 'Why does this have to happen the one day I'm on duty?' 'Where are Liam and Sam?' Hurrying back I almost walk into Brian. He's big and angry. 'This place isn't doing me any fucking good, it's fucking useless,' he roars. 'I've been in months, months, and they've done nothing for me.' He's right, of course. There are no cures for schizophrenia. Perhaps my not disagreeing with him saves my bacon.

Suddenly Mabel is there, electrified hair and all. 'Who are you to threaten everybody?' she screams at Brian. 'Why don't you clear off if you don't like it here? You're just a pain in the bloody arse anyway!' Brian tenses up even more under her onslaught. A tic starts beating in his left cheek.

I drag Mabel off to where some of the other patients are sitting, listening in a tense group, and they hold on to her for me. 'Take her back to her room,' I shout, the pressure getting to me. Brian's stalking off down the corridor, feet crashing down like a robot, heavy with bottling it all in. And where is everybody? I just can't believe they're all busy somewhere else in this maze.

Hurrying round a corner, Brian's suddenly there. Nikki, slim as a model, looks at me with apprehensive eyes across Brian's intervening arm. He's swearing. Good. Keep him talking, talking, talking. Letting off steam. 'No, it's not the fucking nurses!' he shouts, but he won't tell us what it is. I just thank my lucky stars it's not us he's paranoid about.

It might not be us but we're too close, too handy, and he's looking for a target. I speak to Nikki through dry lips: 'Phone Dr Jones up, he'll be able to help. Phone him up, eh Nikki?' She moves over to the phone in the office, out of range of Brian. I haven't a clue what I'm doing. Brian isn't impressed with the idea of talking to the doc. He turns and advances towards me. 'Dr Jones,' he says disparagingly. 'What the fuck is Dr Jones going to do for me?' His voice has risen to a shout by the time he finishes the sentence. I step back a pace, getting out of range myself, and the back of my leg comes up against a chair, causing me to sit down unexpectedly. Brian's absolutely boiling. The aggression is like an actual physical force bubbling up inside him. Suddenly, like a car changing gear, he gains extra power and I know there's no stopping it now.

The partition wall above my head shudders with the impact of the punch. Again and again he hits it, the vibrations running down my spine as I sit, unable to move, below this hail of blows. I expect the plaster to fall off the wall, the hand to be reduced to a bloody pulp, but as so often in psychiatry the normal rules don't seem to apply. Behind Brian I can see Nikki, the phone half lifted, frozen motionless like me. Brian stops, bends his face right down to mine. 'Bastard!' he screams. Then straightens up, turns and walks away. Under control again, for the moment. I feel limp, useless. Am I really in the right job? Nikki comes to life and phones up the male disturbed ward. Ten nerve-racking minutes later Brian has gone.

Nikki sends me off to check the post-ECT patients. A chance to pull myself together. Walter is asleep on his bed, covered by a blanket. Mabel is sitting on her bed in the side room, half turned away from the door. I'm annoyed with her and am just going to give her what for when I notice the blood on the counterpane, pillows and floor. My heart lurches. 'I've done something silly, son,' she says, turning her head towards me. Her arms are lacerated on the insides from wrist to elbow with a criss-cross hatch of slashes. A few of them look fairly bad, the majority just superficial. 'I can't stand another bloody Christmas,' she shouts, as if in explanation. 'I can't stand much more of this carry-on,' I think, wondering what's got into everybody today.

I take her to the clinical room and we look really stupid because I'm holding her arms up in the air to reduce the bleeding. Already she is annoyed that she has not managed to kill herself. Sam and I clean the blood off the arms to assess the extent of the damage. The doctor is coming but it doesn't look so bad once the worst of the blood has been swabbed away. It takes two of us because Mabel's so angry she is clawing at the wounds with her fingernails, trying to open them up. Sam says, 'Next time you try to kill yourself, Mabel, get a sharp knife and stab it into the wrist; these little scratches won't do it.' Sam thinks Mabel is just attention-seeking. 'Where did you get the razor blade?' I ask, knowing all patients are searched when they come in here. 'My husband brought it in for me,' Mabel replies, 'to shave my legs with.' It seems incredible that anyone could be so thick. Having met him, though, I can believe it. The doctor comes, sutures one wound, fixes steri-strips to some more, gives her a jab and leaves. I tidy away the bloody cotton-wool balls and all the rest of the debris. Mabel talks as I work. 'I'm no good, no I'm not, I'm no good.' She's also removing the steri-strips, I notice. I put some fresh ones on, wrap her arms in bandages and fix the ends down with sticking plaster. 'Why do you do this?' she asks me. 'Why do you bother?' She's already pulling at the bandages and it will only be a matter of time until she has them off.

There are now two on constant observation plus an anorexic having naso-gastric feeds who needs watching because she keeps pulling out the tube. A flood of patients are returning early from therapies and there are several old ladies who need to be watched in case they fall. Carol is weeping in the games room but I've no time to find out why because Nikki's just called me into the office. 'Go and sit with Emma Jane please, Buster. Dr Jones wants her on constant observation and I've no more female staff to put with her at present. Leave the door to the room open; that will cover you.' I think once again how all the normal practices which restrict our actions, like male nurses not being left alone with female patients, are happily swept under the carpet when it suits the system.

Emma Jane sits opposite me, that is, in the opposite corner of the small side room she inhabits these days, as a snail lives in a shell. At least she can sit down now that the furniture has been put back in the room. This is an improvement on the mattress on the floor. Though she's not quite sitting. Rather she is hunched forward in the chair. In front of her face she holds a jumper; her face is buried in the jumper. The screams escape from it, squeezing out of the sides and bursting into the room. She has been like this for 20 minutes now, screaming and then rocking. Now and then she says, 'How could he? How could he do that to me?' Then a fresh burst of screaming.

It starts to change. The screaming is abating and instead a gale of tears has blown up. The jumper is now a towel to all intents and purposes. Emma Jane weeps into it. She sobs. She howls. The tears roll forth and saturate the wool. I give her a box of tissues and finally manage to make contact.

We talk for an hour. I take her down from raging temper to accepting a cup of tea; from abusing me to a grudging acceptance; from being incomprehensible to understandable. Emma Jane tells me about her previous suicide attempts and smiles wanly at my amazed response. 'I thought you didn't know,' she says. 'Not after that time in Casualty with Ben.' My mind runs back.

It was hard to say who got the biggest surprise in Casualty, Ben or myself. Probably me, as Ben had just overdosed and wasn't feeling too hot. We were in a bay off the main corridor, Ben was up on the trolley, stripped to his underpants and with just a sheet covering him. I sat beside him but lower down. Emma Jane came walking towards us, that familiar shy smile on her face, the hair swaying gently with her long, easy stride. She smiled at me as she said hello. Then, 'Hello Ben, I'm told you've swallowed some tablets, is that correct?' There wasn't much I could do at that point – she had her own General Trained Nurse to help her – so I went outside and closed the curtains, trying to regain my composure. Trying to see her as a doctor and not as the patient I had been looking after until only a week ago.

'He'll have to have a stomach wash-out.' She spoke from my shoulder, surprising me again. I hadn't heard her coming, but then you never did. She was very natural about it all. 'I've never seen that done,' I ventured. 'Could I come and watch.' 'Of course,' Emma Jane said with a strange smile that only now did I understand: she had had the same thing done to her.

Ben lay on the table and looked up at us. He was pretty scared. I reassured him. Emma Jane also chatted to him, as if it were nothing out of the ordinary to have a large-bore tube worked down into your stomach. The vomit frothed along it and into the bucket. Then she poured the water down the tube and the vomit flowed back up it. Again and again until it was running clear. The last time Ben vomited at the wrong time and we all got a shower of watered-down puke. It was the closest I had ever felt to getting near to her. Swilling the contents of the bucket round to check how many tablets he might have swallowed. Her eyes just inches from mine. That clear and that blue.

I come back to the present and find it hard to compare that Emma Jane with this one, who will not be getting any more chances to practise medicine. Suddenly I feel drained. For an hour nothing has existed for me but Emma Jane. Outside the room is a chair. I sit down on it when I'm eventually relieved because I'm so sapped it's not yet possible to walk away. I still don't know what has upset her or why she's been put on to constant observation.

The world gradually intrudes upon me, lurching into focus like the land seen from a small boat at sea. To do battle is hard enough. To fight without skills is murderous. Nobody has ever shown me how to respond to an attractive young woman as she says, 'I would like to die; to be already dead would be even better.' My blank response, the welling-up of my own hopelessness, seemed the only thing ever to touch Emma Jane in the time just past. Perhaps that was what we had in common.

But there is not much time for sitting around on this acute ward today. 'Buster, go and take that naso-gastric tube out, will you? Felicity is to have something solid to eat every meal from now on.' After removing it herself God knows how many times, it now seems the perverse Felicity does not like the idea of my taking out the tube permanently. It is her certificate of patient-hood that she needs this plastic connection to bridge the gap between life and death; she doesn't want to lose it. She is quite happy to lie abed while her clique, the inadequates, come and pay homage.

As the tube slips backwards out of her left nostril I cannot talk to her. She would like to talk, to go over again and again what a shame it is for her, what a pity it is she has to suffer, how she can't do anything about it, how it's everybody's fault but hers; she would like to eat – 'Honestly Buster, it's just that I can't seem to swallow anything' – but she won't. After an hour with Emma Jane there is nothing left in me now for Felicity, nothing to feel, just an emptiness. The trolley squeaks as I push it out from the dormitory, Felicity crying now behind me.

Some laundry comes. I suggest to Sam that we get a few of the patients to put it away. 'Bloody hell, man,' he replies. 'We'll be here all pigging day if you get that lot of wimps involved. Come on we'll shove the bugger away ourselves.'

'What's got into that fucking Maisie?' asks Sam from the stool he's standing on to put away blankets. 'I always thought she was all right. Fancy pulling a stunt like that.' There's no need to ask what he's on about. 'Maybe he asked for it,' I reply. 'Have you thought about that?' 'Oh come on, man, Martin's been here for years, he wouldn't do something like that.' 'So she just made it up then?' I argue. 'That doesn't sound very likely.' Sam changes tack. 'Look,' he says, 'you just don't do it, not rat on your mates; it's just not on. He could lose his job, you know. And there's no need to stick up for her just because she's in your group.' I let it drop before we fall out.

Afterwards I go and get Walter up and walk him up and down the corridor a few times. He hates me for it, would much rather just sit smoking endless fags, fags that have already cost him a leg with bad circulation. Up and down, up and down, come on you old devil. He's sweating when I sit him back down. That's when I notice Ben, who, like Emma Jane, has been re-admitted. He sits totally immobile – that is, apart from his face. He is hallucinating and unable to respond to me, even when I grip his arm and shake it gently to gain his attention. He laughs and smiles at something better. The room has a large clique of inadequates in it. They laugh between themselves, at Ben, at me trying to talk to the boy, at anything positive anybody ever does. My colour rises with my anger, which gets somewhat displaced on to Ben; I'm shaking him too roughly. 'Come on Ben, come with me a minute.' There is a sniggering laugh behind me from Mary Chambers and I'm within a very short distance of blowing. Then Liam is there, helping me pull Ben to his feet, keeping him upright while we walk him out of the room. 'All right, take it easy,' Liam's saying, as if to Ben, but we both know that it's me he's really talking to.

Ben has wet himself while hallucinating. We put him in the bath, I fetch clean clothes. Liam goes to get the soiled chair out of the sitting room. When he comes back to help me get Ben out the bath he's laughing. 'Guess what?' he chortles. 'Mary Chambers is sitting in Ben's chair.' Now we're both laughing and Ben, lying in the bath, is laughing too, though not with us. 'She'll get a surprise,' Liam gurgles. And the temper dissipates. And the emptiness.

'Did I ever tell you about the old boy with the verrucas?' I ask him. 'No, don't think you ever did,' says Liam, drying Ben. 'Well it was when I was on my first ward: came in one morning, switched the lights on in the dormitory and there's this old boy just walking down the ward crapping all over himself. Well, I found him so I got him to do. I start to take him to the bathroom and Gloria, who was on there then, shouts at me, 'Don't take him through without covering him up.' So I wraps a sheet round him and start again. Then she decides he's got verrucas on his feet and I'm not to walk him through because they'll spread all over the place. I mean to say! Now the problem is his feet are covered in you know what. Well I get an inspiration and put two

83

paper towels on the floor. I get the old fellow to stand on them and of course he's got so much crap on his feet that they stick. So off we go to the bathroom, him flapping along looking like some sort of ancient mystic frogman with the sheet and the paper towels. Well, to cut a long story short I wash him down and give him a good soak, then when I'm getting him out the bath I notice all these white marks all over his back. I haven't really got a clue what they are but then I remember Gloria saying he had verrucas. I get Sister to come and look at him. "What's up?" she asks. "He's covered in verrucas," I tell her, "all over his back." "Verrucas?" she says disbelievingly. Anyway, in she comes, looks at his back and then gives me this pitying stare. "Do you notice anything strange about these verrucas?" she asks, "Like for instance that they're all keyhole-shaped and they're all in straight lines! He's been lying on the bath mat, you daft idiot," she laughs. "It's the impression off that."' 'Oh no,' says Liam grinning, 'you wally.' 'Don't tell me,' I agree. 'She still reminds me of that every time I see her.'

I find myself sitting on the end of Felicity's bed. The food already cold on her plate, she is counting the chips. 'There's twelve!' she exclaims petulantly, 'How can I ever eat twelve chips as well as all that fish? If I eat the fish can I leave the chips?' 'You know the answer to that, Felicity,' I reply. She argues. 'But why must I eat twelve chips? I don't need twelve chips, surely. The doctor didn't say I'd have to eat that many, not twelve. And there's 27 peas! Why can't I have my tube back again? Why can't I?'

Felicity is quite repulsive for me to look at. It's not that she weighs just five stones, has arms like sticks, a head like a skull – no, the worst thing is that she thinks she's attractive and keeps fluttering her eyelids at me coquettishly. The gap between what she thinks she is and reality is an enormous one. Her consultant comes in at the top end of the dormitory and walks down towards us. By the time he has reached us she is howling at full blast. 'They're making me eat all these chips,' she wails. 'I've had ever so many but they say I've got to eat them all.' I leave him to it and step out into the nurses' station.

'Go and get yourself changed,' says Gloria. She is wearing a track suit tucked into a pair of football socks at the bottom, and trainers. I had almost forgotten the game was today. It doesn't take long to pull on my kit. Sam comes in while I'm changing. 'Did stick insect have any lunch?' he grunts. 'Not as you'd notice. A cod's head, six chips and a couple of peas at the last count.' 'What a fucking waste of time that girl is,' he says, tying his laces. 'I'm telling you she'd be straight out that fucking door if it was up to me, manipulative little bitch.'

The Annual Christmas Rugby Match is played on the hospital pitch, which this year has about a foot of snow on most of it and considerably more where it's drifted. Being an annual event it usually attracts a few spectators, but there's only about 25 here today, none of whom are patients. The only patients one ever sees on the playing fields are the occasional masturbator and a load of old chronics who, weather permitting, escape down here out of the way for a kip. 'I don't think we'll have any trouble spotting you in the snow, Rosemary,' quips Sam and gets a snowball in the ear for his trouble. Being a mixed-sex game nobody takes it too seriously. A few little feuds are literally kicked into touch and the frustrations of the morning's work are soon dissipated. Snowballs rattle about in a constant barrage. I notice Maisie is getting more than her fair share of them and go across to give her some support.

When things quieten down a bit I ask her, 'What's on your mind?' Most of the men are indulging in a spot of groping, which is evident but not excessive, and it seems a shame there are no patients here at the moment to observe how mental nurses behave without their uniforms to hide behind. 'Och, it's nothing, Buster. Forget about it, eh.' She brushes the snow slowly off her clothes. 'Come on,' I reply. 'I've a good idea what's going on, you know. I'm not daft.' A great shudder seems to run through her. 'I've . . .' she starts to say, just as the ebullient Rosemary cannons into my back, sending me head over heels in the snow. 'Hey Buster,' she laughs, jumping on top of me as Maisie chases away after the ball, 'how do you fancy a bit of black?'

Afterwards we adjourn to the despised Social Club where we

compare injuries and gulp down the long drinks. The pint of ale slides down my throat in quick pulls and my healthy glow is soon accentuated by an alcoholic flush. George comes in and I remember my promise to buy him a pint. He looks terrible. His hand shakes when he picks up the drink and he has to hold it with both. 'You want to take it a bit easier,' I tell him. What Joanna said comes back to me. 'Listen George, are you all right?' I ask him seriously. For a while he just stands there as if he's not even heard me. When he eventually comes back to the present and looks at me there's something in that glance I recognize from the wards. Something furtive, something hopeless, but I can't put my finger on it. Then, without a word, he walks away and sits down on his own. I've had too much beer for logical thinking and take the hump. 'Cheers mate,' I say to myself.

The pile of glasses on the table grows larger and larger, as we drink way past the official closing time and Emma Jane, Dorothy, Felicity, Ben, Brian, Edna, Walter, Mabel and all the rest become forgotten. Even George, who sits drunk and alone. None of us has yet changed and it doesn't seem to matter that I am still in my kit and wearing some woman's fur coat when we all clamber into the back of a taxi, clutching various shapes, sizes and colours of bottles and tins, heading for a piss-up.

By the time we actually get back to my house, the many who set out have dwindled by half a dozen. Not that we're despondent, not with all that drink and a variety of silly games designed to help us drink it twice as fast. I find myself on all fours, one female sitting side-saddle on my back – a girl with a laugh like cannon balls rattling on a hot tin roof – and another feeding me lager at the front. The laughter grows and swells and moves. Laughter at anything, laughter at laughter, laughter at memories, laughter at the morning's work, laughter as a shield we use to protect ourselves against the insane hospital.

Now I'm on the settee, flat on my back, where Maisie's drunken rugby tackle and Rosemary's shove have landed me. Maisie's lying stretched on top of me, where she landed. Somehow she's wearing the fur coat I came here in. I can feel each spasm of her laughter, which feels to be getting stronger by the minute. Until I realize she's crying. Her shield dropped, defences breached, clamping me hard against her. Sobbing into the gap between my neck and the back of the settee, 'Oh Buster, Buster, why are they like that? I was only doing my job. Why are they so nasty to me?' I keep her there, stroking her through the coat, hiding her distress, until she settles.

Showers are suggested and every now and then a face disappears from the group around me which is singing a strange mixture of Christmas carols and rugby songs. Somebody brings me the phone and I call Anne who arrives home from work armed with extra bottles picked up from the off-licence. She laughs at the sight of me, half submerged under this sleeping red-headed bear. Rosemary comes back into the front room damp and not properly dressed, having showered in half her clothes. 'I don't want to worry anybody,' she says seriously, 'but I've just set the egg-timer off.'

Saturday 22 December

I've been here before and expect a quiet shift, but when I come on duty there's a body lying in the kitchen with two nurses busy working over it. One of them has the patient's mouth prised open while the other is trying to remove whatever it is he's choked on. A few feet away, in the dining area, several patients are sitting drinking cups of tea, paying no attention to the drama behind them. I get the job of phoning for the doctor.

The day charge nurse arrives 20 minutes later, on the dot of seven, by which time the patient is breathing on his own again but still deeply unconscious. We put him to bed and the night nurse offers to stay on and look after him until he's moved.

After the sour-faced middle-aged charge nurse, called Mr Brown, has received Report he comes into the dormitory and points at me. 'You do breakfasts,' he says – no please, thank you or good morning. It's no more than I expect, having worked with him before. I curse his missing staff, an SEN and a nursing auxiliary, who are no doubt still tucked up in their beds, using the weather as an excuse for stopping away from work.

We give out breakfast in silence. 'Don't pay any attention to that miserable old fart,' Zoe, the young ward maid, tells me. 'He's just in a mood.' The breakfasts come ready plated and while I run about dishing out meals Mr Brown pulls the plates out of the trolley and puts them on the top where I can get at them. He's taking something to eat off nearly every plate, tearing bits of bacon off with his hands and shovelling spoonfuls of scambled egg into his miserable face. 'You dirty bastard,' I think. One of our ageing schizophrenics, Donald, asks for scrambled eggs and then refuses to eat it. 'He's trying to starve himself to death, that one,' says Zoe, about Donald, when Mr Brown goes off to get the medicine trolley. I'm glad somebody's telling me what's going on.

Mr Brown comes back looking like an eight-draw man who has forgotten to post his coupon. I become re-acquainted with a particular little trick he likes to work on students at the medicine round, hustling them into making mistakes and then pulling them up for it. I'm trying to put patients' faces to names and he's walking off with bottles of pills in his hands, dishing them out left, right and centre before I can work out who's who. 'Come on, come on,' he snaps, almost looking cheerful. 'We haven't got all bloody day, you know.' I'm putting pills out into pots and he's shaking them out into his hands, walking over to patients and pushing them into their mouths, then asking for the next lot of tablets before I've even worked out who it's for, never mind recorded it properly.

When he gets to where Donald sits with the scrambled eggs uneaten on his plate he stops dead in his tracks. 'I hope you're going to eat that lot up.' His voice is quiet but menacing. Donald mumbles something I can't hear. 'Come on, get it eaten up,' Mr Brown shouts. 'I don't want this shit,' says Donald, and we all hear him that time. Next second Mr Brown has his hand round Donald's neck and is pushing his face down into the plate. Donald tries to jerk back out of the way but can't. Mr Brown rubs his face into the plate, absolutely unable to control himself. 'Not good enough for you, is it?' he rasps. 'Well if I say you're going to eat it, you're going to bloody well eat it.' It takes him a few minutes to regain his composure and then he goes and gets a cloth from the kitchen and wipes Donald's face. It's almost an apology.

After the patients have had their breakfast we have our tea. The doctor still hasn't been to see our unconscious patient but that's nothing unusual. Long-stay and geriatric patients never get anybody in a hurry. We sit around the table and nobody speaks. Zoe pours Mr Brown's tea first. He tastes it, gets up, goes into the kitchen and pours it down the sink. Zoe purses her lips in annoyance but goes and makes him another pot. This is another of his little mannerisms that one gets to know. He tastes the cup from the second pot, smiles, and drinks. Zoe and I drink ours in silence until he goes to telephone the doctor. 'I've had enough of that sod this morning,' Zoe says. 'What's wrong with him?' I ask. 'God knows,' Zoe replies. 'Just keep out of his way until it wears off. You know what he's like when he's in a mood.'

Mr Brown comes back and he and I go to do the injections. He draws them all up; there are six to do. Then I call the patients. They all know his routine and stand outside the clinical room door with their trousers and underpants at half mast. The first one comes in, bends over, and I do the honours with the needle. This happens six times in as many minutes and then they all troop off to work, still pulling up their trousers.

'You go and do the beds,' Mr Brown growls. I can tell he's taken against me this morning but can't put my finger on why – if there is a why! He's just a moody old devil and always has been. A 40-year man who came here as an attendant in the days of 'knuckle therapy', when the only requirements were a strong arm and an aptitude for sport. Now he's a dinosaur. Out of time. Out of place. Becoming extinct. There's a new order creeping in, albeit ever so slowly, against which he fights a rearguard action.

The beds are low divans. Thirty of them. I make the first six beds standing up, then have to do the rest on my knees to give my aching back a rest. The night nurse, who's still hanging around, gives me a hand with some of them. In one bay a patient I don't know from Adam is fornicating with an old-fashioned radiator that is turned fully on. But not by him. I chase him off to work, his erection wagging along in front of him.

The doctor comes to do the patients' medicals, an annual requirement. I'm sent out to round them up. Our unconscious patient is still on the ward so the doc has a quick look at him and then transfers him down to the hospital sick ward – what the long-stay patients call 'Death Row'. The night nurse gets himself off to the Nurses' Home where, like a few others, he's got a bed for the duration of this bad weather. And somebody to keep it warm for him if the rumours are correct. I get the patients to queue outside the charge nurse's office and the doctor calls them in as he wants them. Nobody is in longer than five minutes and nobody gets undressed to be examined. Mr Brown tells me to make a note of these momentous events in the patients' nursing records. I notice their care plans have not been updated for two years.

I do the baths and Mr Brown nips home to feed his pigeons. He's been doing it for years but nobody ever says anything to him. There are only four patients to bath. The bathroom has no curtain between the two baths. Two patients get in, ignoring each other, while the other two stand outside the open door. I go to close the door but Donald tells me Mr Brown doesn't like it being shut. When the first two are still getting dressed the second two come and have their baths, all four of them in the place at the same time. One of the patients is hung like a donkey. 'What a waste,' says Zoe, looking in from where she's washing the floor in the corridor and giving me a very friendly smile. Donald, stark naked, turns round and blows his nose on the curtains.

The nursing auxiliary I'm covering for arrives unexpectedly after managing to dig herself free of the snowdrift into which she skidded at 6.30 this morning. I feel guilty for thinking she was dodging off work. She certainly looks done in and Zoe gives her lots of tea and sympathy. Mr Brown, who has returned from feeding the pigeons, sends me off with two patients for the long-stay Therapy Department. 'Report to the Nursing Office,' he growls without any further explanation. He appears to say nothing apart from what he has to say, and that reluctantly.

The Therapy Department is well known to me. It is the pits. If you are a student and get allocated here then you know you are in for six weeks of solid boredom. I go in with my patients and sit down with the staff for a cup of tea. There has never been a time when I've called here and not found the staff making tea, drinking tea, or washing up after a cup of tea. The soon-to-be-retired nurse in charge of this dive is called Mrs Fanshawe.

The patients sit around in a haphazard fashion doing very little. Some are putting bits of shammy cloth on a string to make a wash leather. Trouble is that at the end of every session the staff take the shammy leather off the string to use again, so none is ever completed. The bits of shammy are greasy and blackened with age and frequent handling, year after year of being stuck on and taken off again. No wonder the hospital is so economical to run. In deference to the festive season a few of the patients are making paper chains. There's no sponge-pad for them to wet the gummed paper with so they have to lick the piles of individual coloured squares themselves. One patient paints endlessly, always a variation on the same picture, others knit wash cloths. A couple are making table decorations, with candles and holly, for their wards. I ask the man who's painting if he is looking forward to Christmas. There's no reply but his picture gets a Christmas tree stuck in the corner of it and I get a grin.

After tea some of the ladies do some baking. The staff weigh out all the ingredients, put them in a bowl, stick a spoon in and hand it to the patients. The patients then stir for as long as they want at the mixture while the staff have another cup of tea. Then the staff come back, stir the mixture again, even if the patient has done this properly, and put the mixture out into the trays. No wonder the patients look uninterested. It is a standing joke among the students that every week a bakery order from the kitchen arrives which includes chocolate, cheese, fruit and endless other goodies. And every week the patients make rock cakes. Well, nearly every week. I see today's efforts are centred on the inevitable mince pies – which will no doubt go the same way as the ingredients. Outside, a long-stay patient is sifting through a dustbin in search of fag ends with which to make a roll-up.

Two men are making gnomes. 'Fat Fanny Fanshawe's Gnome Factory' is what the wags call it in here. Mrs Fanshawe, who must have been shown the subtle art of making gnomes at some point in her career, has two patients turning them out remorselessly under her personal direction. When I first started my training the hospital was overrun with them, you couldn't open a cupboard without a gnome leaping out at you. Then suddenly they became fashionable – the pundits said because it was the only place you could get gnomes with deformities, which was true. Most of them had bits missing or lumps added on; some were hideously twisted, others hardly recognizable. Whatever the reason, she sold out at the last Gala Day and it now looks as if she is going great guns again to get stocked up for next summer's event, judging by the pile of hideous monstrosities at one end of the room.

I go to take a closer look and get a nasty shock. Fat Fanny Fanshawe has branched out. Behind the pile of gnomes I could see from the door are row upon row of hideous little men in red and white suits. Every one a Santa Claus! There's a Santa with a foot at 90 degrees to his leg, one with a nose missing, another that would look the same lying or standing. The paint on most of them has run, and on one, an albino Santa, the red and white have been substituted one for the other. The amazing thing is, though, that they've all got sold tickets on and are just lurking here waiting to be launched upon an unsuspecting world.

At the Nursing Office I'm told to finish off my shift on a rehabilitation ward that has some patients going into town shopping and needs extra cover. I protest that I haven't worked on it before but to no avail. 'Well now's your chance, son,' croaks my role model, fag between his lips, fat hanging over his belt, reading the *Sun*. What's the point in arguing?

As I go in the door of the rehabilitation ward the Sister, a homely-looking woman who looks like she's in her late thirties, is leading a patient towards the stairs. 'You are in a really bad way, Mac,' she's saying to the patient. 'In fact I don't think you are going to make it so I'm going to help you upstairs and put you to bed.' The patient looks a bit quizzical. 'Do you mean I'm really ill, like?' he asks. 'Ill?' the Sister says, shaking her head from side to side. 'Yes, you certainly are ill.' I step to one side, concerned for this poor old fellow who sounds as if he is about to peg out. As she walks past, the Sister smiles at me.

Inside, the nursing auxiliary is sitting filling in the ward menu. But I've never seen anybody doing them like this before. There are charts of fibre content and books of calorific values. 'Hello,' she greets me warmly, and shakes hands. 'Listen, are you any good at maths, I'm doing this project on diets in relation to mood-swings but I just can't work these calorific values out.' With that I was into it. A teaching session, but so enjoyable I don't even notice I'm having it. Or that it's an auxiliary who's doing the teaching!

The Sister comes back down and shakes hands. 'Hello Sister, I'm . . .' I start to say, but she interrupts. 'Call me Jayne,' she introduces herself. 'And we know you, Buster, even if you don't know us. You're one of the good guys. Now what do you know about "paradoxing"?' 'Oh don't let her start on that,' Jean, the auxiliary, laughs. 'You'll never shut her up.' Jayne, unperturbed, explains why she was telling the old man he was ill when he wasn't, and I begin to understand it. 'The thing is, Buster, that the old man has got into the habit of complaining he is ill. His life revolves in a sort of pattern around that fact. Now everybody has a natural resistance to being told anything; what we're trying to do is build upon that resistance. If we tell him he's ill, and he wants to resist what we're saying, then he has to argue that he isn't ill. To argue that he also has to think it and before you know it the pattern is broken. In a nutshell, what we're doing is telling him he can't get better, that he can't change, but in such a way that he can change.'

Jayne finishes her explanation and makes it clear that she wants me to use this approach whenever I have to talk to the old man, that it's a technique she now expects me to apply. Suddenly I feel threatened. What kind of a place is this? I start to remember phrases like 'revolutionary' and 'go-ahead' that other students have used about this ward.

After telling me about paradoxing Jayne goes and fetches a small tape recorder out of the office. 'We tape-record all reports on here,' she informs me. 'That cuts down hand-over time, saves money and provides us with a permanent record during the whole shift. Let's listen and see what Bertie's got to tell us.' She switches on the tape and a man's voice booms out into the room.

'Right Jayne, just one or two little things for you tonight. Charlotte is lying on the floor outside the office door pretending to be dead. This hysterical behaviour has been going on all night and she may still be here when you come on in the morning.' Bertie's voice changes to a shout, obviously at the recumbent Charlotte. 'Charlotte, if you get up right now I'll give you a fag.' Then, more quietly, a few moments later: 'Well Jayne, she may really be dead because that didn't move her either. Watch you don't trip over her body when you come on tomorrow.' The subject changes. 'You may notice Joyce isn't here when you get in tomorrow. The reason is that she's over on the female disturbed ward. Usual thing. Shouting, swearing, carrying herself on. In the end she took a swipe at my auxiliary so she's gone over there to cool down.' Jayne switches the tape off. 'I'll tell you what that's all about,' she says. 'She's run out of fags. They'll give her any amount on disturbed so she's played up to get herself in there. Don't always assume disturbed behaviour is related to mental illness. Joyce uses it to get just what she wants.'

Bertie's voice continues. 'Thanks very much for not sending off that accident form while I was off. Mr Neale has been on the phone and given me a right bollocking!' Jayne switches off again. She's laughing. 'Oh God, I forgot all about that accident form. I bet Neale was going potty, cos I promised it to him days ago.' Bertie's voice comes back on: 'That's the lot for now. The money for your trip up town is in the drawer. 'Bye.'

We have a cup of tea with the patients. Jayne introduces me to all the patients in the day room. The staff don't have their own cups or chairs or anything else. I notice that the chairs are all placed in groups around tables and not stuck back in the usual position against the wall. Ada, reminiscent of the Queen Mother but far more bejewelled, starts talking to Jayne. 'Inside my belly is a huge bee, the moon flows out of my mouth when I speak, there are cowboys and Indians inside my head, war-dancing on my neck.' Jayne answers; 'Did I tell you when I was chopping down daffodils and Santa Claus hopped out of the bushes singing "It's a White Christmas"?' Ada looks at her closely. 'Go on, you're crackers you are, you daft bat,' she says after a long pause.

Jayne moves in. She gets locked into an intense five-minute conversation with Ada. 'Reality nursing,' she tells me afterwards, 'that's what I'm trying at the moment. How can you act insane if you have to know the difference between normal and abnormal? These people are afloat in this ocean of madness we call a hospital. If we act daft when they do then they can't drift happily along relying on us to keep them from drifting on to the rocks, they have to learn to look out for themselves. A lot of these people talk rubbish because they've always been with other people who talk rubbish. They may not be mentally ill but they are certainly institutionalized into exhibiting a load of secondary symptoms.'

Charlotte comes in for her cup of tea as Jayne finishes talking and Jayne gets up and fetches the tape across to where Charlotte sits with the other patients. Jayne runs the tape back until she finds the bit where Bertie is reporting on Charlotte. 'I want you all to listen to this,' she says to the room at large, and turns Bertie's tape on at full blast.

'Charlotte is lying on the floor outside the office door pretending to be dead. This hysterical behaviour has been going on all night and she may still be here when you come on in the morning. Charlotte, if you get up right now I'll give you a fag . . . Well Jayne, she may really be dead because that didn't move her either. Watch you don't trip over her body when you come on tomorrow.'

Jayne addresses the patients. 'This is the same Charlotte who wanted to be given a flat on her own, mind. The one who reckoned there was nothing wrong with her.' Ada speaks out: 'She's bloody daft, Sister. It's locking up she wants, not putting out.' 'You can shut up, Ada,' snaps Charlotte. 'You're just jealous.' 'Jealous of you lying about on the floor all night,' sneers Ada. 'I don't think so, dear.'

Jayne explains to me the reason for putting Charlotte's behaviour to the group of patients with whom she lives. About them exerting social pressure on her to act more normally; about the milieu of the ward as an agent for changing behaviour. Behind her is a blackboard on which staff and patients leave messages. In large letters it's got today's date and the words, 'CHRISTMAS SHOPPING'. I'm not looking forward to the trip. People looking at you shepherding round groups of misfits, nudging each other and pointing, turning to stare after your departing backs; younger people laughing out loud, older ones saying, 'Ah, poor souls, they can't help it.' And always somebody waiting to plummet you up to the eyeballs in embarrassment.

I follow the nursing auxiliary upstairs to check the dormitories are OK and to try and absorb some of what Jayne has been telling me almost non-stop since I came on to the ward. Nobody tells me to help her. In fact nobody is telling me to do anything and I'm feeling exposed to my own inadequacies. After three years of training I don't seem to have any initiative left at all. I can't understand how Jayne has arrived at this point in her career, in this hospital, with so much skill and vision. She has a real knowledge of what is going on around her, not some medically or psychologically stereotyped knowledge but a deeper insight, almost an extra sense, of what makes the patients tick.

To my dismay most of the beds are only half made and a couple still have patients in them. 'Oh no, I've just made one lot of beds up,' I complain, my feelings towards the ward rapidly cooling. Jean smiles. 'There's no beds to make on here,' she explains. 'The patients make their own. If they don't make them properly it's them that has to put up with it; they've all been shown how to do it. As for those in bed, well that's their decision. If they stay in bed they don't get any breakfast. They all have to take the consequences of their acts. This is a rehabilitation ward, you know.' I feel out of my depth. This is all heresy. 'But what if they don't go to work?' 'Then for a start they don't get paid, which they hate because it cuts down on the fag money, and if they persist they get the sack – you see, it's just like the real world.'

Downstairs most of the patients are doing an exercise and movement class under the direction of a blue-rinsed lady from the occupational therapy department. 'That's a good idea,' I say to Jayne, trying to get on her wavelength. 'I'm trying to get it stopped,' she answers. 'How many of this lot are going to do exercise and movement when they're discharged from here? It's unreal and it puts them in a passive role: they have to follow directions. That's no good here.' 'Oh,' I answer. Jayne laughs at my expression. 'Don't worry about it,' she says. 'Just look around at what's going on and try to learn something from it. I know it's hard to break out of the mould.'

The old fellow upstairs gets a cup of tea and a biscuit and I convince him he's definitely on the way out. I find Mr Neale upstairs as well, he's come in without anybody seeing him and is obviously sneaking round the dormitory seeing what's what. He's the nurse in charge of the hospital today. 'Come on and I'll show you how to make a bed,' he says. I don't think it's my place to point out to him that the patients on here make their own beds. 'Anyway,' I think, 'he knows that.' 'Now the essence of making beds is to do it with the minimum of effort,' he pontificates. 'You should never have to move your feet. Just sway from one end to the other.' I spend the next ten minutes watching this rather corpulent character going through the most tortuous motions I've ever seen in my life, as he tries to put his theory into practice. He loses his balance twice and by the look on his face he might have put his back out. We end up with a badly made bed and a red-faced, perspiring Mr Neale. I wonder what's happening to the rest of the hospital while he's mucking about in here playing silly devils.

He leaves and I have a wander round the ward. Some patients are doing their own washing and ironing, others are knitting or reading or smoking or just about anything they want to do. Two of them are adding to the decorations on the Christmas tree, which is getting decidedly lopsided under their ministrations. I start to cross the room to sort things out but Jayne catches my eye and indicates to leave them alone. Eventually the inevitable happens and the whole tree topples over on to a dozing Ada, who gives the two culprits a surprisingly lucid tongue-lashing. Without the staff doing anything the three of them resolve their differences and the tree is resurrected under Ada's careful scrutiny. 'Put the bloody fairy on the top,' Ada shouts. I feel that I'm learning something but I'm not sure what it is.

One patient is watching the television which is discreetly placed in a small alcove off the day room. Another aberration from the norm. He rubs his head when he talks to me. Jayne comes in and rubs her head. He stops rubbing his head and gives a small laugh. 'Sorry,' he grins at her. 'Rub away, Gavin,' Jayne replies. 'I don't care if people laugh at you.' A frown crosses Gavin's face. 'They won't laugh at me, will they Jayne?' he asks. 'Well what do you think, Gavin?' she replies. 'Wouldn't you laugh at somebody who rubs the top of their head every time they talk to you?' Gavin reaches for the top of his head. 'Jayne,' he says, then laughs, having made a joke at his own expense. We all join in and laugh with him, which is nice. The walls are covered in charts saying things like 'Discharge Plan', 'Miles Run', 'Trips to Town'. All are inexpertly filled in, from which I know the patients are doing them.

Jeffrey comes in and says he can't find his razor. I spend ten minutes looking for it. 'What you after?' Jean asks as I pass her for the third time upstairs. When I tell her she laughs. 'Come with me,' she says mysteriously. Back downstairs Jeffrey is sitting comfortably in his chair having a nice cup of tea. 'Now we are supposed to be rehabilitating the patients on here,' Jean says patiently. 'Do you think he's doing anything for himself?' I get a little hot under the collar at this mild attack. 'But if he doesn't know where his razor is . . .' I don't finish. With an understanding smile Jean lifts her hand to signal I should stop speaking, then turns to Jeffrey. 'Are you going up town today, Jeffrey?' she enquires. 'Yes, I'm going for a pub lunch with Jayne,' Jeffrey replies. 'Then you better go and have a wash and a shave,' Jean tells him. 'But I don't know where my razor is,' Jeffrey responds. 'It's your razor, Jeffrey,' says Jean meaningfully. 'And if you don't get organized there's no way Jayne will take you with her.' We walk off.

Jayne is also in the day room but I don't spot her for a moment because she's curled up in a chair completely covered by a blanket. I follow Jean out into the kitchen and ask her what's going on now. 'Oh, she often does that,' Jean tells me. 'The patients forget she's there after a few minutes and stop putting on their usual act. It's a good way of finding out what they're really like. You know, who's friends with who, who's the boss, who stirs it up, that sort of thing.' I'm not sure if I'm in the presence of an idiot or a genius. Jean tells me what their discharge rate is and that they have no re-admissions. I plump for genius.

'Of course they are trying to break the ward team up,' Jayne tells me later, when I mention that Mr Neale had been sneaking about. 'That's why he was upstairs. Looking for some more ammunition to fire at us. He'll complain about unmade beds, patients not getting up when they are supposed to, patients not going to therapy. We've had it all before. One day he'll succeed and stop the whole thing dead in its tracks.' 'Oh come on,' I argue, feeling a bit more confident with her than I did at the start of the shift. 'That's a bit paranoid, isn't it? Why on earth would Mr Neale want to stop what's probably the only successful ward in the hospital from functioning properly?' 'Because we are not playing by the rules,' Jayne explains patiently. 'We are the living proof that the system is rotten, that the system doesn't work, that you have to beat the system before you get any success. He represents the system. What we are saying then is that he has got it wrong and we have got it right. We are not only saying it, we are proving it. There's not another rehabilitation ward in the region to match ours and he can't let that continue. If he does, then one day he'll be out of a job. Because in our way of working there's no need for nursing officers. No need for any senior nurses to work in the hospital. No place for him or the system that allows him to exist. We do it all despite him, not because of him. Don't you see? It's all politics.'

Behind us Jean has set up a bus in the middle of the ward by the simple expedient of placing most of the chairs in two rows with an aisle down the middle. She ropes us in. Jayne drives and I get the job of conductor. The patients are given the task of going into town on the bus. One or two refuse to play and say its silly. The rest join in happily and we spend half an hour enjoying ourselves and learning. Some patients don't raise their hands to signal the bus to stop so they get left behind. Others, it turns out, don't understand the new decimal money, even though it's over ten years old, and can't work out how much they need to buy a ticket. Others don't know what to ask for when they get on board. I'm absolutely amazed at the amount of things this simple bit of role-play throws up, identifying areas of the patients' functioning that need to be worked on. Of course, with the trip going out into town today, it's also topical.

Jayne and I go up town with the patients who have expressed a wish to do some last-minute Christmas shopping. Jeffrey has shaved himself and got ready and I've learned something else about rehabilitation. I've been on millions of trips out with patients and know what the score is. Staff act like shepherds, moving patients around, supervising them across the road, doing everything for them, keeping them free from stress. I'm in for another surprise.

'What time's the bus going back?' Jayne asks. 'Quarter to two,' Jeffrey answers. 'All right, be back here for then,' Jayne tells them. We all stand there looking at one another. It soon gets pretty cold. I look to move away towards town but Jayne covertly pulls at my sleeve and gives a discreet shake of her head. After about five minutes the first of the patients walks away and soon the other three are following him towards the nearby town centre. We stand until they've all gone. I feel terrible, especially as little Jeffrey trundles off after the others. It's my duty to look after these people, to protect them from harm. And here I am letting them go into town alone at the busiest time of the year. 'Let's go and have a coffee,' says Jayne. 'What about the patients?' I ask anxiously. 'Let's go and have a coffee,' she repeats. It's almost impossible for me to let them go. I'm wracked with guilt thinking of all the things that could go wrong and scared of getting into trouble if anybody has an accident.

We have our coffee and Jayne explains her idea of rehabilitation. Taking risks is what it's all about, especially for her, though she doesn't say that. Give patients the opportunity to cope, the chance to make mistakes and learn by them. 'Some of these people have been in hospital for 30 years,' she explains. 'They have got to learn about the real world all over again.' I'm not convinced. 'Look, you or I could go out there and get knocked down by a car,' she says. 'That doesn't mean we have to spend the rest of our lives in this café, does it?' 'But we can cope with traffic,' I argue back. 'They can't.' 'Who says they can't?'

Jayne interjects. 'How do you know they can't? And if they can't, shouldn't we be allowing them the opportunity to learn how. They will never look left or right when we're with them, they are all institutionalized, they know you will look for them. That's why they are out there now and we're in here, so they can really learn.'

I soon decide that Jayne has more in common with a guru than a Sister. You can't listen to her for long without being converted to her way of thinking. Yet it's diametrically opposed to the majority view, the view that has been hammered into me for the last three years – not by a process of education, but by a process of indifference. We spend the rest of our time in the town centre, which admittedly is quite small, discreetly observing the patients. They've paired off and, after buying what they want, two of them settle for lunch in a café and two go into a pub to get their food. They all get something to eat, they all stay somewhere warm. Nobody gets run over, nobody gets lost. They all turn up at the bus station on time, apart from one patient who's decided to have a few more drinks and catch a later bus. 'Do you want me to go and get him?' I ask. 'What for?' Jayne answers with a note of exasperation. I start to see: this is a breakthrough, not a problem. It's me that has the problem. I'm institutionalized. And the realization makes me very sad. Because I never thought I would be. Other people yes, but not me.

Back on the ward Jayne has the medicine round still to do. It's late but she doesn't seem concerned. She wheels the trolley into the day room and then sits down beside it. She doesn't shout 'Tablets!' or call the patients' names, as usually happens. The medicine trolley is open for business if anybody wants to indulge. 'The patients have to take responsibility for their own medicines,' Jayne explains. 'When they leave here they'll have to do it themselves so we might as well start as we mean to go on. We don't force any psychotropic medications on patients who don't want them, though obviously we would make sure anybody on such as insulin gets their prescribed dose.' This is unbelievable. The drug round is sacrosanct. But here Jayne is giving the patients the final say over what happens to themselves. Jayne assures me the use of tablets has dropped dramatically over the last year since they decided on this course of action – and without any corresponding increase in disturbed behaviour.

Jayne has given the report into the tape recorder, so the actual hand-over time is dramatically reduced and is used instead for teaching. 'Right, tell us about schizophrenia,' Jayne instructs me. I go into the classification, signs and symptoms, types of medicines. 'Are you training to be a doctor?' Jayne queries. 'Look, this is schizophrenia.' We pull a chair out and sit two others at the side of it. I sit in the middle, Jean and Jayne sit each side of me, and another student, off the afternoon shift, talks to me, as a nurse would, from the front. As she talks so do Jean and Jayne. For the first time I get an insight into what it must be like to try to hold a conversation when hearing voices yourself. Trying to concentrate on one voice while hearing others seems impossible. 'That's more like schizophrenia,' Jayne laughs when I give up, a couple of minutes into the experiment. 'Remember it next time you are talking to a schizophrenic.'

A few students from other wards start to drift into the room. It appears Jayne often runs informal groups between shifts for anybody who wants to come along. She takes me to one side. 'Look, Buster,' she says, 'I want to do something on how we react to aggression. Do you think you could act really angry and storm out of the room during this session?' I'm reluctant but she talks me into it and we get the group under way. I sit there feeling scared of making a show of myself, and without knowing it convincing everybody that I'm not my normal self. The session continues and I try to get into the part I'm supposed to act but it just doesn't seem to come. All the time I'm getting more and more wound up at my failure to act, at the thought of letting Jayne down, at the prospect of making an arse of myself if it doesn't work out properly. Then suddenly I get hot – that's how I experience it – and I find myself getting slowly to my feet with what must be a maniacal stare because everybody stops dead. 'I've had enough of this fucking shit,' I bellow at the top of my voice. 'Talk, talk, talk. That's all we ever fucking well do in this place. Well I've had enough of it. I'm off.' Jayne goes to say something to me but I'm really quite out of control. 'And you can bloody well shut it too,' I yell, before turning and storming out of the room, nearly kicking the door off its hinges on the way.

I wind up in the day room and there's so much adrenalin pumping round my body that I'm unable to stop myself shaking. I pace around and around, which seems to help, and then I start feeling euphoric. It's impossible to suppress my smiles and the laughter begins to bubble out of me. When Jayne comes out of the room to find me I'm convulsed with laughter, doubled up with the effort of trying to catch my breath, bumping into things. The room has gone quiet. Then there are tears rolling down my face and I don't seem to know why or to be able to do anything about stopping them. Jayne gently takes my arm and leads me away through the silent patients to the empty kitchen. 'What's up with that daft sod?' I hear Ada ask. 'Buster's fired a wobbler,' Charlotte says quietly. Then we're in the quiet of the kitchen and Jayne's holding me, saying softly over and over again, 'It's all right, it's all right.' A wonderful soothing warmth seems to flow from her, so that a short time later I'm able to rejoin the group not much the worse for wear. 'You swine, Buster,' one of them says. 'You frightened me to death. I thought you really meant it.' 'No, only kidding,' I say. 'Nothing to worry about.' 'Right,' says Jayne. 'Now I want you all to tell me how you felt when Buster got to his feet and started shouting.' Instead of this I think about how much I suppress my feelings. About how badly I needed that outlet for my anger. Then I look at Jayne and realize she also knew it.

I think about the shift on my way home. About the difference between my first ward and my last. About how good I feel without that familiar knot of anger tying up my stomach. About how Jayne could have known it was there. I wonder how two such wards could exist within the same hospital. How a charge nurse and a Sister exposed to the same influences could turn out so differently. Most of all I wonder what I'm going to turn out like. What Maisie, Rosemary and Joanna are going to turn out like. What any learner is going to turn out like when pitted against the institution. It seems to me the odds are steeply stacked against any of us ever following in the footsteps of Jayne.

Tonight is a big night at the hospital, with the staff's Christmas Dance held in the concert hall. This year there is the additional spectacle of a fancy dress competition. Anne and I go, as much to get out the house as anything else.

It's the usual sort of effort with a bar set up in one corner, a group on the stage, and a fair-sized dance area surrounded by lots of small tables stacked with drinks. I find some friends for Anne to sit with and go for the drinks. Apart from the fact that it's the concert hall I could still be in the Social Club. All the regulars are standing at the bar, they're even in roughly the same positions. A few of them are already the worse for drink.

The first excitement of the evening is the presentation of certificates to last year's students who passed their final examinations. As I watch, a horrible thought crosses my mind. If 90 per cent of our students and pupils pass their finals, which they do every year, then the standards in other mental hospitals must be the same, and in some cases worse, than they are here.

It's the room going quiet that tells me something is happening, and when I turn round from the bar, where I'm fetching another round of drinks, there they are. Rosemary is dressed as Captain Hook and Joanna as Peter Pan, complete with pyjamas. I wonder what on earth they're dressed like that for and then remember the fancy dress competition. I look quickly round. They're the only two in here who have bothered.

'Oh God,' Rosemary groans to me when she arrives at the bar, 'I feel such an idiot.' 'Rosemary, I'm going to do you in one of these days,' says Joanna, arriving hard on her heels. 'You and your bright ideas.' 'It's not my fault,' Rosemary defends herself, gesticulating with her hook. 'It's all these miserable buggers.' The voice of the compère for the night, who usually calls the bingo in the club, comes across loud and clear. 'I see the first two competitors for the fancy dress competition have arrived. It's Peter Pan and Captain Hook if I'm not mistaken. Well done, girls.' 'Rosemary,' hisses Joanna under her breath, as everybody's eyes swivel round to look at them and there is a burst of laughter, 'I'm going to bloody kill you.' I get them both a couple of quick doubles and they're just settling down to see the funny side of it when the compère's voice booms out again. 'And I do believe that here comes little Tinkerbell,' he says, not without a touch of sarcasm. Joanna and Rosemary exchange horrified glances. 'Oh no, she'll kill me,' says Rosemary, quailing, but even as she speaks the room goes quiet again.

Maisie stands in the doorway. She's hideously overdressed in something that looks like Shirley Temple's party frock. Her hair is full of ribbons and she's carrying a bamboo 'wand' with a yellow cardboard star stuck in a cleft at the end of it. On her feet she's got a pair of green wellies. She stumps across the silent room towards us, coming to a standstill eyeball to eyeball with Rosemary. For a moment neither of them speaks. Then Maisie starts to laugh. It begins somewhere down around her knees and bubbles up and out into the room in an infectious hoot. 'Rosemary, you silly bitch,' she laughs, in a room becoming full of laughter, 'where the hell have you put my bloody shoes?'

Sunday 23 December

A twisting, seedy, urine-stinking stone staircase leads up five flights to the ward. Luke, the staff nurse, whom I met coming across, unlocks the door and we go inside. There is a dull finality as it slams shut behind me that induces a lasting feeling of claustrophobia. At a solid 17 stone, with no visible join between his head and his shoulders, Luke's presence is very reassuring. Though the blond streaks in the hair don't do a lot for him. In the day room, patients' heads turn in their chairs to see who it is. One of them gets up and walks awkwardly across, a stubbly head of irregular spiky hair over a permanently twisted face. He holds out his hand and makes gooing sounds. Luke sticks his own massive paw out and they shake. 'Super Sid!' Luke says. 'Want a piggy-back?' Luke asks, crouching down in the appropriate position and smiling encouragingly. Sidney gets on his back and Luke gallops off up the dormitory with him. Sidney's repulsive face is split by a large grin when they come back. Luke lets him down and we go in for change-over. I feel relief as the heavy office door snaps shut behind me.

'Aye-aye, where is everybody?' Luke asks. 'And what are you doing here, you toe-rag?' The last remark is addressed to Sam, the staff nurse I'd worked with two days ago on Acutes, who obviously knows Luke well as he smiles back at him. 'You'll be glad of all the help you can get this afternoon, pox-features,' he says genially. 'Get yourself a cup of tea and I'll tell you all about it.' As Luke pours, Vernon, who's a fellow student, and Eric, a nursing assistant, also come in for Report. Sam waits until we've all got something to drink and then he tells us what's been going on.

'He came in during the night, about four o'clock. Billy Scott they call him. Well, first thing this morning he's at it. Going round telling everybody he was the New Messiah and that he'd come to save the world.' 'Oh no, not another fucking messiah,' says Luke with feeling. 'That's two now, it must be the Christmas rush starting.' Sam continues, 'So we put him to bed after the first scrap, intending to keep him there nice and quiet like until we could sort him out. When he found out he was for a day in kip he went radge. "I was in the fucking Marines," he shouts at Micky, "and no fucking ponce in a white coat is keeping me in bed." Well, what a battle! We had to send for reinforcements to get him in the lock-up; they were coming from everywhere. Even our do-lally nursing officer got his coat off and gave us a hand.' 'I'd have liked to have seen that,' Luke interrupts. 'Did he break into a sweat?'

Sam laughs and sips his tea before continuing, seeming more at home in this macho environment than he did up on Acutes. 'Hold on, there's more to come. That was about half past nine. We put the seclusion policy into force and checked him every fifteen minutes through the spyhole. When the two-hourly door-open check came round and we went in to see him he'd only gone and lost his fucking ear!' Luke laughs grimly: 'Ha, I bet that went down well.' 'You can bloody laugh,' Sam goes on, 'but have you ever tried to put an emergency dressing on someone's head while they're trying to deprive you of your nuts? It was chaos!' 'How'd he do it then?' Luke queries. Sam shrugs. 'Hard to say. It might have got ripped off against the door because he hit it like a ton of bricks when we were trying to shut it on him. There's also a lot of blood around the lock so it may be he'd caught it on there and torn it off.' 'Where is he now, up the General?' 'Yeah, four of them have gone with him. Micky even had the sense to pick up his ear and stick it in a bag of ice.'

My heart shrinks as Sam relates the story of the morning's events. The other odd punches, kicks and scratches recounted hardly seem worth bothering about in the light of this character's adventures, especially now we're waiting for him to come back. We go and prepare for his return.

The seclusion room, known to all staff as the lock-up, contains an indestructible carpet that, if you happen to be dragged along it by an irate patient, as I have been in the past, gives you friction burns. There is nothing else in the room but a mattress on the floor. The window is shuttered with a single large key-hole letting in the only light from outside. There are two grids up near the high ceiling to let the air circulate. A single bulb behind a protective shield casts a bare light on the shocking-pink walls. I question the colour, which is new. Apparently some Canadian psychologist found it was the best colour for reducing violent behaviour. I don't believe it.

Blood is streaked across the walls and door and shutter, presumably where the Marine has been wiping his hands on them. It looks like there's been an accident in a sweet factory. Eric wipes down the walls and door. I get on my knees and put a sheet on the mattress. Being in here reminds me of the first time I visited the place, when I was still on my first ward.

It was a lovely summer's day and the walk to work had been a real pleasure. Then I heard a voice hailing me from the bushes. It was Sam, then a newly qualified staff nurse. 'Buster,' he shouted, popping up from the middle of a clump of bushes, 'run up and tell them that he's going towards the main exit.' With that he disappeared back into the undergrowth.

The charge nurse took his car at the double when I told him and off we screeched, picking up Sam along the way. A short stocky man came into sight. He was dressed in pyjamas, carrying a Tesco bag and wearing slippers. We screamed up beside him and Sam was out and after him like a bull at a red flag. The guy took to his heels but Sam was too fast and quickly ran him down. You can't get much speed up in a pair of slippers. The charge nurse and I followed, leaving the car slewed across the road. When we cannoned into the struggling pair it seemed to wind the man for a second and the four of us went down in a heap, me holding on to a flailing arm.

'He', whoever he was, seemed to get his strength back and the four of us slithered about among the shady trees. One minute I was facing the sky, a clear summer blue, the next my nose was in the grass. After a few minutes of this struggle the man quietened down, the charge nurse talking to him all the time. Some female nurses were watching us from a nearby ward and, half shouting, half gesticulating, we managed to get the idea across to them that they should phone for some help.

Because the man had gone quiet I relaxed my grip so as not to hurt him. It was my first experience of handling a violent patient. Splat! His fist pushed my bottom front teeth through my lip and rocked me back on my heels. I locked back on to his arm, my head ringing, and vaguely saw other figures in white coats swarming out of the hospital. The man was firmly gripped by dozens of hands and born aloft like some spoil of war to be carried in triumph to this ward. That was my introduction to the disturbed wards. Of course, when I got back to my own ward it was to find out that the chap we had just captured, stripped and incarcerated hadn't even been a patient, as he was still waiting to be admitted when he took off! Fat Jack came up from the school and was in his element, tut-tutting, when he read my statement, so I felt as if my days as a student nurse were numbered. It all blew over of course; these things always do. It's the one area where the team really works. The cover-up.

After preparing the side room it would suit me just fine to go back into the office and lock that big heavy door behind me. Instead I go through into the day room and start to re-introduce myself to those patients I know and let the others get to know me. Most of them are already familiar from other wards, or from around the hospital if they have ground parole. That helps a lot to steady my nerves until I spot Brian sitting in the corner, staring at me from behind a haze of cigarette smoke. Brian, who only the other day had been thumping the wall above my head on Acutes and calling me a bastard! He doesn't speak but his malevolent presence fills that corner of the day room. The bruised and swollen face of Dan, the charge nurse on here, is still fresh in my mind from the day that Brian walked into the office and broke his nose with a punch out of the blue. Brian's the sort of man you need to develop a sixth sense for.

'Are you on here now?' Kenny, a long-time patient, asks me, diverting my attention from the glowering Brian. We start chatting. He's taking the opportunity to unburden all his moans and complaints to a new face, but I'm so relieved to be doing something half normal in this oppressively abnormal atmosphere that I don't mind at all.

The door-bell rings. My stomach muscles tense. 'Pete, you daft bastard, what are you doing with that? Buster, come and look at this,' Luke shouts me. At the door stands an incredibly tall, thin man. He's hidden by the fridge that he's just carried up five flights of steps. 'Bloody Nora!' exclaims Sam, bursting into a loud guffaw as he too comes to view the scene. 'Where's he picked that up from?' 'It's from the Nurses' Home,' Vernon informs us. 'He's always pinching stuff out of there.' Reluctantly Pete places the fridge down outside the door and Sam goes and rings the porters to come and take it away while Luke gets Pete a fag from the locked drawer in the office.

I'm told to keep an eye on him while he's got the fag on. Pete sits in an orange chair. There are so many holes in it from fag burns it's hard to see how the fabric holds together. His clothes are similarly spotted with brown-edged holes and he and the chair seem to merge together. The fingers and thumb that hold the cigarette are scarred and blackened from smoking dog-ends, stumps, rolled up bits of newspaper and almost anything else that will burn, including tea-bags. His lips are covered in blisters and scabs from the same cause. Sidney goes across to where he's sitting. 'Fagggg,' he says, holding out his hand to Pete. Pete breaks the fag in two and gives half to Sidney. 'Super Sid,' he shouts, giving him a light from his own half of the cigarette. I watch fascinated as, instead of smoking the fag, Sid uses the lit end to singe the stubble on his head. I get Luke but he says just to leave him alone as he's always done it and gets aggressive if you try to stop him. Sidney limps off into the space between the chairs and the wall.

Hearing the door open I walk through to see who's coming. It's the morning staff returning with Billy Scott. He's big, about six foot six, and what they used to call raw-boned. His head is swathed in bandages and I notice that the skin on both his hands, across the fingers of which are tattooed 'love' and 'hate', is torn and ragged. They walk him easily into the seclusion room and lock him in. There's a visible relaxation in the group as the door's three locks are closed on him.

'Buster, you big ugly get,' Dan, the returning charge nurse, greets me, 'don't tell me you're on here today. I've got enough problems without you adding to them.' Besides Dan there's a couple of guys I don't know and Micky, a tough-looking nursing auxiliary who I know and like from my last stint on this ward. They're all high on adrenalin and cracking on. Dan, more macho than ever beneath a new moustache, gives me his key. 'Go and make us a tray of tea you good-for-nothing student bastard! I'm gagging.' It's his normal mode of speech and I take no offence as none is meant. I go into the kitchen, never thinking to lock the door behind me, and switch on the boiler. Not knowing where anything is it takes me a while to put the contents of the tea-tray together. Brian comes in! I don't exactly wet myself and fall on the floor but it's a pretty close thing. 'I want a drink of water,' he says, staring at me. Speechless, my hand searches out a cup and gives it to him. He goes to the boiler and fills the cup. The water isn't boiling but it must be very hot. He gulps it down and then takes another. Brian comes right up close to me, almost standing on my toes, and hands me back the cup. His face absolutely expressionless, 'Thank you,' he says. 'Any time, Brian,' I squeak.

We leave one person out on the ward and the rest of us pile into the office. The morning staff are all still pretty excited and the story comes tumbling out. 'What a bloody farce that was, bucko,' says Micky. 'The bloody ambulance ran out of petrol!' 'You what!' exclaims Luke, butting in. 'Ran out of petrol?' 'Yeah, right in the middle of nowhere,' Dan cuts in. 'There's four of us holding on to that clown and suddenly the engine cuts out and we glide to a standstill.' Micky again: 'It wasn't very nice calling the driver a brainless, cross-eyed fucking wally,' he laughs. 'Well, of all the stupid fucking carry-ons. What did you expect me to say?' 'You should have known better than to try getting to the General in that beat-up old wreck. It's only fit for taking stiffs to the mortuary,' says Sam. 'So what did you do?' asks Luke. 'Do? What could we do? Them two got out and pushed while me and Micky sat on that bugger. Trouble was we couldn't hold him so they had to get back in again.' Dan stops to sip his tea. Micky butts in: 'Fancy kicking the driver out in that snow without a coat to fetch some petrol,' he joshes Dan. 'Serve the stupid bastard right,' replies Dan, taking the bait. 'I hope he catches fucking pneumonia.' 'You can't actually catch pneumonia,' says Vernon, who's a bit of a prat. 'Has anybody ever told you you're a fucking prat,' Dan growls. Vernon shuts up. 'So what have they done with his ear, then?' enquires Sam. 'Did they stitch it back on?' 'No, there's no point. When we got it cleaned up there's still half his ear left, though a bit pulpy like. If they'd tried sewing the rest back on that crazy bastard would just have pulled it off again. They've just tidied it up and stitched it.'

Dan gives us another Report, aided by Sam, and I discover we have someone coming in this afternoon who has tried to shoot his psychiatrist with a crossbow. 'Though why that should be grounds for admission I can't think,' jokes Dan. In the middle of Report our nursing officer arrives. I know him from previous wards. He's just a joke. After asking about the patient in seclusion he says with a manipulative smile, 'Ah, Dan, I wonder could you do me a little favour this afternoon?' 'No,' Dan says brusquely. The nursing officer is taken aback. He doesn't realize Dan is just making an arse out of him. 'Oh,' he says, 'if that's how you feel about it, but you could at least give me a chance to get my request out.' 'All right then, what is it?' Dan asks impatiently. 'I need someone to do overtime for me, we're short on several wards with this bad weather and I just haven't got anybody to give you the extra cover you need on here.' 'You mean,' Dan says, looking at his watch, 'that you're coming here half an hour before we go home to ask someone to do a double shift!' 'Er, well, I realize it's short notice but – ' Dan interrupts again: 'It seems to me it's always short notice!' Having made his point Dan changes his tack. 'Look, this is what I'll do for you. If you are paying overtime and none of that time-back crap then I'll do it. If not, forget it.' The nursing officer looks defeated. 'OK. My budget is going to look terrible but I can do that.' 'And,' Dan cuts in again, 'I'm going home for a couple of hours first to get my dinner and have a break from this spot.' There is no argument.

Vernon, who's junior to me, follows me and Dan up to the seclusion room. Dan opens the three locks, first shouting through to Billy that he should sit down. Inside, the atmosphere is heavily oppressive. Billy has urinated up against the wall. 'Now are you going to behave yourself, Billy? Because if you are I'll leave these two lads to talk to you and that door can stay open. If not I'm going out again and locking it for the rest of the day.' Dan stands aggressively, hands on hips, face jutted forward, leaning over the seated Billy. 'Billy Scott, Lord of the Cosmos,' Billy says, looking up. Dan sighs. 'OK, we'll try him anyway,' he says, turning towards us. 'You two have got the first hour and then someone will come up to relieve you.' It's five months since I've been on this ward. Now here's old 'love' and 'hate' Billy Scott, with his head all bandaged up like a skull cap, and myself and Vernon, incarcerated together. The trained staff take to the office and Eric is left out on the ward.

'What's your name?' Billy asks Vernon. 'Vernon Carter,' he answers. 'Vernon Carter, everything he wants, a fuck a day, the money to pay,' Billy says, looking heavenwards. 'What's your name?' he asks me. The speech is repeated using my name instead of Vernon's. Billy slumps forward slightly, he's fighting the drugs all the time. Knowing what he's had, I'm surprised he's not unconscious.

'How long are you going to keep me locked up in this fucking hole?' Vernon and I have both squatted down but now, as Billy gets awkwardly to his feet, we both stand quickly up again. 'Just stay there, Billy,' I tell him. 'You heard what the boss said.' My palms are sweating. 'I'm staying fucking nowhere,' Billy shouts, looking me straight in the eye. Then he slumps down again. After a few minutes we relax and squat down as well. 'What's your name?' he asks Vernon. 'Vernon Carter,' Vernon replies.

'Vernon Carter, everything he wants, a fuck a day, the money to pay,' Billy says. 'What's your name . . .'

'They killed him, them bastards.' Billy talks almost non-stop now. A lifetime of harsh reality bursts out of him in a tormented twisted tale of unbelievable deprivation and hardship. From fear my feelings swing round to something like understanding and then back to fear again. 'I'm just going out here, all right?' Billy is pushing Vernon and me backwards, not physically but by advancing upon us. He's determined to get out this time so we back-pedal until we're on the dormitory. There's no need to shout the others. They are on their way as soon as we appear outside the seclusion room. We surround him, engulf him and put him back in with only a verbal struggle. Billy is bitter for a while and gives us the evil eye. Then he comes round again. 'What's your name?'

This time he's talking through his delusion. 'I just want to help people,' he tells us. 'I don't want to hurt anybody. That's why I became the Lord of the Cosmos. My message is peace. There was this girl in Holland. I really loved her; it wasn't just because I was fucking her – no, not just for the fuck. But we lost contact. Now I've got to get back and find her, don't you see?' Again we retreat under Billy's advance. The others back us up and we push him back into the room. We could just leave him locked in but then you have to put the seclusion policy into operation which is a real hassle. 'Any chance of a fag for fuck's sake?' Billy shouts. 'It's not going to cost you anything is it, you miserable bastard?' Then for a while he goes quieter. Perhaps he's dozing. Vernon and I relax.

The hour has long since passed and we should have been relieved. Looking down the dormitory towards the office I see all the qualified staff inside laughing and carrying on. It looks like they're having a pre-Christmas drink. Catching Luke's eye and pointing at my watch to show him our time's up brings forth a gale of laughter and a V sign. It seems we are stuck with it, at least until Dan gets back.

For a while it is interesting, even exciting, as Billy keeps getting up and trying to leave the room. We don't know if he's going to jump us or what and the adrenalin flows freely. Then we seem to burn out. The whole thing becomes an enormous strain that presses in like a physical force. The strain of the endlessly repeated conversations; the tension rising time and time again; the endless quiet periods with Billy dozing, Vernon and I keeping quiet in the hope he will stay that way; having to watch our own actions all the time so that he isn't threatened by our movements and triggered into violence; the constant barrage of abuse every time he wakes up.

Sometimes, shut up with the Marine, it seems as if the world has stopped. Drag is not an adequate description of what time does at such moments. It's almost a relief when Billy starts talking rubbish again, especially when he gets on to the subject of his circumcision. 'I've been circumcised you see,' Billy says, 'but it's an immaculate circumcision so that my foreskin's still there.' Vernon and I looked puzzled. 'Have any of you two been circumcised?' he asks us. 'I have,' Vernon says foolishly. 'Take out your prick,' Billy tells him, standing up, 'and I'll take out mine and you can see what I mean.' He's fiddling at his pyjama bottoms. Vernon's on the spot but he manages to bluff, he saves exposing himself at the cost of reinforcing Billy's delusions. 'No it's OK, Billy, I know what you mean now, an immaculate circumcision! Right, I'm with you now.' Billy never shows the slightest discomfort from his injury.

Eventually we are relieved. If that is the right word for coming out of one small mad room into a much larger mad ward. The business with Billy is like a pebble dropped in still water. The ripples spread out around the ward and everybody becomes more and more edgy. Dougie has been put to bed as a punishment for bothering the other patients. He looks up quickly, startled, as we walk past him. Then suspicion spreads over his face. We are just walking into the office for a well-earned cup of tea when there is a rush of feet behind us. Turning quickly, we see that Dougie is charging at us with an upraised chair. 'One,' he screams. Everything stops. There he stands, pyjama jacket open across a broad, out-of-condition torso, chair above his head, fair hair tied back in a pony-tail. He looks surprised. Then he puts down the chair and goes back to bed. Brian comes and asks to go out. 'Tomorrow,' he's told. It doesn't please him but he knows the system.

'Come and watch this,' Dan shouts down the ward to us some time later. 'This' is a young swarthy alcoholic called Leo. I've nursed him on several wards and remember looking after him at the General the morning after he tried to kill himself. None of the other staff on the medical ward there would talk to him. An 'overdose' who was distraught because the other alcoholic he shacked up with had killed herself, he didn't have a lot going for him in their eyes. I just tried to imagine what I would feel like if Anne had died. Then it had been easy to help him.

Today Leo looks nervous as he's prepared for his first Antabuse session. A bottle of vodka is produced. 'OK Leo, try a drink of this.' Leo's nervous, he doesn't really want to drink but I can see he can't stop himself, even though he knows the tablets he's already taken will make him ill. 'S-s-some Christmas this is going to be,' he stammers. After the first drink, about a treble, he looks OK. He wants another now but the doctor makes him wait a minute. Leo starts to flush and begins to sweat. Still he wants another drink. Dan gives me a bucket – 'In case he's sick.' The second drink brings Leo out in a bright red flush, the sweat is rolling off him now. 'I feel sick,' he gasps, and I hold the bucket in front of him. He isn't sick, though he clutches at the bucket and moans. 'You see how bad it is,' the doctor says to him. Leo looks up with a feeble grin. 'It always makes me sick when I have the first few mouthfuls,' he says. 'I can't stand the taste of alcohol.' He drinks the third glass and starts retching, though he's not actually bringing anything up. Leo holds his head and rolls about, sits up, lies down, trying to find some relief. 'Oh my fucking head,' he groans. It's pretty barbaric even to have to watch. Leo starts heaving up and I stand there steadying the bucket for him.

When it's all over and everyone's gone, with Leo tucked up in bed, the weaselly Eric slides into the clinical room, which I'm still tidying up. He winks at me, takes the bottle of vodka and has a good long slug. Then another one. He tops the bottle back up with water and puts it back where he found it before stealing off again. A few minutes later Dan comes back as I'm rinsing out the bucket. 'Better lock this vodka away,' he says, 'or that bastard Eric will drink it all before nine o'clock.' He locks it away in the drug cupboard.

Out on the ward, and out of sight, I hear Dougie shout, 'One.' 'It's all a waste of time you know,' Dan says about Leo. 'He'll just throw those tablets away as soon as he gets out of here. Might as well not bother at all.' 'Can't you get implants though?' I question. 'Oh sure, if they don't fester and fall out; they hardly ever take properly. And they affect everybody differently so some people have them in and still carry on drinking. They're not as good as they sound. Besides if an alcoholic really is going to give up drinking he needs to do it himself. At least the tablets allow him to choose. He doesn't need any commitment at all for the implant. Leo will be back in, you wait and see. They all come back.'

I go out into the dormitory just in time to catch Dougie climbing on top of the locker beside his bed. I catch his leg and pull him down. He doesn't want to come. When he hits the ground he starts jumping wildly around, kicking out one minute, hopping on one leg the next. He looks terrified. I have to let him go and he runs up the ward, turning over a bed on the way. Dan comes out of the clinical room as Dougie charges back towards me carrying a locker on his back. Together we stop him and manage to get him back into bed. He lies there looking round and whimpering. It's hard to believe he used to be a staff nurse here.

'Buster, get Pete for us will you, he's creating havoc on Geriatrics.' Geriatrics, when I get there, is in confusion. Some visitors are sitting apprehensively by the bedside of a dying patient. Two nurses are comforting another old lady whose misshapen arm looks good cause for the howls she's emitting. 'Where is he?' I ask the staff nurse in charge. She's pretty mad about it all but she doesn't take it out on me. 'He's in the third side room down. We can't get him out.' Pete is lying in the old lady's bed, his feet sticking out the bottom. The sheet is pulled up over his head and smoke is coming from underneath it. 'Come on, Pete,' I tell him firmly. 'Dan wants to see you.' He doesn't move. Pulling back the sheets reveals that thin, elongated face lying on the pillow, fag between the lips. 'Come on Pete, let's go.' Pulling his feet towards me swings him out of bed. 'I've got to search you, Pete, in case you've got anything of the old lady's.' He's quite passive as my hands run through his pockets, taking out compacts, Christmas cards, make-up and lipsticks. 'Boodle,' he says, looking at it. 'You hurt her you know, Pete. The doctor's got to come and see her.' It's impossible to tell how much gets through to him. He raises a bloodshot eye and looks at me, then pushes past and walks towards the exit.

Back on the ward Eric opens the door. 'Get in here, you bastard,' he says to Pete, grabbing him and pulling him in. He kicks him up the backside and Pete goes running off up the dormitory shouting, 'Eric – you – Eric! Bastard Eric!' 'Skinny cunt,' Eric mutters under his breath. Dougie is rolling about, arms flailing, on the dormitory floor. 'Look at that soft bastard,' Eric tells me. In a few minutes Dougie gets up and goes back to bed. I go and talk to him. Or rather talk to myself. He's preoccupied and I can't even get an acknowledgement off him. Pete is still shouting.

Dan opens the office door and shouts me over. I get a four-foot-high stuffed frog, a book of raffle tickets and a tin of money shoved in my hands. 'Buster, you silver-tongued charmer,' he says, 'go and sell them tickets for our Christmas raffle and don't come back until they've all gone.' The frog's huge and I wonder how I'm going to carry all this stuff. Then I remember there's a wheelchair in the sluice so I go and get it to put the frog in. Trouble is I turn my back for five minutes and Super Sid gets into it instead. I give him the frog to hold and take both of them downstairs in the lift. There's not so much between them when it comes to looks. Outside the kitchens a patient comes across and looks down at Sidney. 'Fuck me,' he says, 'Super Sid! I thought you were fucking dead!' Sidney looks up and laughs at him.

I tour the wards, selling tickets and collecting kisses under the mistletoe. On one of the back wards I sell a load of tickets to the girls on duty. Tessa, the SEN I've assumed is in charge, goes into the darkened office to get her handbag so she can pay me and a charge nurse is briefly revealed, blinking in the light of day. 'Want to buy a raffle ticket?' I ask him civilly, not having realized before that anybody was in the office. He doesn't answer. Tessa closes the door on him again. 'Don't worry about old misery-guts,' she whispers, scrabbling in her purse. 'He's hiding in there until we've got all the work done.'

I'm having a good time, wandering about the hospital with my two passengers – though judging by the response it seems some of the staff think Sidney is the prize – when Vernon catches up with me and tells me I've got to go back. It appears the charge nurse off Tessa's ward has phoned up to complain that I went on the ward without letting him know I was there and without asking permission to sell tickets. 'Christ, can't you do anything properly?' Dan bollocks me when I get back.

Time for more tea. The ward maid makes it before she goes off duty. What a big mouth this one has got, and she's only pint-sized. Still, it's not a job to attract the shrinking violets. We do the crossword in the *Mirror* and try to ignore her rabbiting on. Sidney walks up to the table. 'Sidneeee,' he says, reaching for a cup. 'Fuck off, Sidney,' Eric snarls, slapping at the outstretched hand, 'Give us a minute's peace for Christ's sake.' Sidney goes off up the ward at speed. 'No tea. No tea,' he shouts over and over. 'Fucking hell, Eric, did you have to set him off,' Dan says, only half joking. Sidney comes back down the ward, his fists bunched as he flies past us. 'Watch yourself,' Dan says, but I need no second warning and lean back out of range. Luke grunts, 'He can't half give you a bloody clout.' Billy has become much quieter and we put him to bed, where he goes straight to sleep, the drugs having at last caught up with him.

We start the medications. Some of the doses are unbelievable. Brian comes for his tablets and syrup. He's brooding and stares at me as I put his prescribed medication up for him. There's enough to stop an elephant at fifty paces. Suddenly he grabs the water jug off the trolley. It's nearly full and he tips it up and starts to drink. The others cheer him on as he gulps mightily, water spilling down the sides of his mouth and over his face, neck and chest. He nearly makes it to the bottom but not quite. 'Feel better for that, Brian?' Dan asks sarcastically, giving me the two-litre jug to refill. Brian takes his medicine and goes back to his seat. 'Keep your eyes open for him,' Dan tells me, as if I needed any second warning. 'When he starts doing daft little things like that it's usually a sign he's going off.' We finish by taking the medicine trolley round to the patients in bed. Billy we leave as he's really flat out now and hopefully shouldn't be any further trouble today.

Next it's the evening meal to dish out and supervise. Sidney has quietened down, Pete has got worse. Dougie is still hallucinating. Mealtimes are always a high spot for trouble on any ward. Psychiatric patients have a very low tolerance of others. Crowd them all together in a room and problems inevitably arise. Tonight it's a mouthy young psychopath who has been withdrawing off drugs. He's sitting opposite Brian, an act of bravado on his part as Brian doesn't like anyone sitting close to him. 'You can't half eat, Brian, eh,' the psychopath is saying, 'Good old Brian. That's some gut you've got on you, boy.' 'Shut it,' says Dan from behind the serving hatch. 'Just get your dinner eaten.' 'Oh aye, who the fuck are you to tell me to shut up? You're just a nurse, you. You take orders from doctors and I'm going to see mine and tell him what you said. Me and Brian's all right, ain't we, Brian?'

Brian's eating. He concentrates hard on his food, eats both his dinner and his pudding, tries to get seconds from the serving hatch and fails because he needs to lose some weight. The bunched hand smashes into the psychopath's face so fast it's not visible. There's just Brian walking off up the dormitory and a body slumped back against the wall on an overturned chair. I expect to see blood but there isn't any. The others keep on eating as Eric and Luke take the unconscious psychopath off, slung between them, to sort him out.

Pete gets over-excited and is banished from the dining room for shouting. He goes off down the ward but we can still hear him. Now and then he tries to get back in, as he's not finished his dinner, but he's chased every time which only makes him worse. The atmosphere is tense. Sidney throws his rice pudding on the floor.

When the patients have had their meal I go for my tea. There are spare meals on the patients' trolley but on this ward I need to get away for a break. I'm hungry for some non-macho company and enjoy the 20 minutes which I have to eat my meal. This place is usually a study in miniature of the hospital. Doctors at one table, workmen at another, students at another. No signs. Just a refusal to mix. Today, being Sunday, there's only one person in who isn't a nurse.

I hear the door open behind me and recognize the voice without having to turn round. Besides, somebody at the table says, 'Huh, look what the cat just dragged in.' I make a point of turning round and shouting across the room, 'Hey, Maisie, come and sit with us.' I get dirty looks from two of the girls at the table and they get up and leave. Maisie appears impervious to it all. 'Phew!' she exclaims, sitting down, her plate heavily laden with chips and not much else. 'What's this I hear about you trying to ride me the other day when I was drunk?' Maisie accuses me, 'You dirty old man ye.' I play her game. 'Hold on, Campbell, as I remember it you were the one who had the leg over me.' 'Och well, that's all right then,' she laughs.

Lynne, the Sister off Geriatrics, comes and sits with us, as do a few others. I start to realize that there's more to this Maisie business than meets the eye. I get a feeling that the hospital is polarizing into camps. And there's no middle ground. The tension drains off me as we sit talking, the shoulders start to loosen up, but before I'm completely relaxed it's time to go back to the ward. As I'm going out of the door Maisie shouts across the crowded canteen, 'Hey Buster! You're a great screw!' Raising eyebrows on a few more sour faces.

The other staff have had their dinner on the ward and are drinking a cup of tea in the office when I return. 'I see Taff's retiring off nights,' says Eric. 'He's been retired for years, that one,' grunts Luke. 'When I was a pupil, during my nights up there he used to go to sleep at ten o'clock and get woken up at six with a cup of tea by his nursing assistant. She used to look after the place.' 'Oh aye, he's lazy,' Eric agrees, 'but he's a good laugh. I remember that day Freddie Jopp got his tablet stuck in his throat. Quick as a flash Taff ran round the trolley. 'Bend over, Freddie,' he shouted, and then kicked him up the arse real hard, which did the trick. Freddie couldn't thank him enough!' 'I remember,' says Luke, 'when some psychopath, I've forgotten her name, came up to us at midnight saying she had to have her bed moved as she couldn't sleep. Well Taff looks at her very sorrowfully like and explains, "I'm very sorry, we can't just move beds about as and when we like. We'd never know where anybody was. You'll have to apply to the bed allocation officer, in triplicate, and then we'll sort something out." So off goes this psychopath, happy as a lark because she thinks she's causing some trouble, and sits up half the night writing out three times why she wants to be moved.'

Kenny knocks on the door and we let him in. 'Give us a fag eh?' He moves from foot to foot, standing in the doorway; nobody answers him. 'Give us a fag eh?' he asks again. 'It's not time yet, Kenny,' Luke says. 'Go on Kenny, piss off.' That's Dan. Kenny smiles ingratiatingly. 'Shut the bloody door after you,' Eric snarls at him. 'Give us a fag eh?' Kenny asks. They ignore him. He stands there, shifting his weight from foot to foot, his face getting redder and redder. The tears spring to his eyes. 'Why won't you give me a fag?' he sniffs. 'They're mine, why can't I have one?' 'Don't you start fucking howling,' Luke tells him. 'Go on, piss off.' Kenny advances into the room; he's sobbing now. 'I hate you lot, I'm going to see Dr Jones and tell him you won't give me a fag.' 'Go on then, fuck off,' Luke tells him. But Kenny doesn't move. Eric gets up and starts to shove him out the door. Kenny is too strong for him though, and Eric can't budge him. Luke goes to help, he's the biggest bloke on the staff, but still they can hardly move Kenny. Luke loses his rag. 'Right, Kenny, you're going in the seclusion room. I've fucking well had enough of you.' They half drag, half push him through the office door, though he clings to the frame desperately, like a drowning man. 'What are you putting me in there for?' Kenny sobs. 'I've done nothing wrong.' They're in a heap now on the floor. Kenny doesn't hit out but he's just so strong that they're getting really mad at not being able to shift him. I give them a hand to try and get the business over as quickly as possible. Even so we struggle all the way up the dormitory with him. At the door of the seclusion room he gets another burst of strength. Luke is really mad now. 'I'm fed up with you, you snivelling bastard,' he rasps, hitting Kenny in the middle of the back with his knee. Kenny folds and we throw him into seclusion. I feel dirty.

The ward gets a bit of a bustle on when our new admission arrives, minus his crossbow. More trouble is taken over his physical state than his psychiatric problems, which I've learnt is normal in this hospital, where the staff have the skills to carry out physical care but no skills to deal with psychiatric problems. Dougie, who is in the next bed to the new man, gets excited by all the to-ing and fro-ing and ends up swinging off the curtain rail round his bed, pulling it down around his ears just as some visitors call to see him. I show them into the now empty dining area and then fetch him down to see them. Pete is still shouting and carrying on.

In the sitting room there isn't a chair free of fag burns. The TV is high up on the wall, out of reach of the patients. The walls, once pastel colours, are now dirty orange with cigarette smoke. I talk to anyone who wants a conversation. The psychopath comes back in to sit and watch telly in his dressing gown and pyjamas. His lip is split and puffy and he doesn't have anything to say for himself.

Kenny is let out of seclusion after ten minutes and is fine. He smiles and laughs and seems to have forgotten what he was put in there for. He asks to go out and is promptly shoved out of the door. 'Don't rush back, will you?' Luke shouts after him. I have a game of pool with Vernon, who beats me easily. Pete comes bouncing in, shouting and carrying on. We shut him in to give him a chance to calm down and when I go back to see how he's getting on he peppers me with pool balls, which I guess is his way of telling me to get lost.

More tea. The bustle dies down but we have our tea out in the dining room because the ward is so restless. 'It must be you, Buster, you big get. It's normally quiet as the grave in here,' says Dan. 'Well at least he got stuck in and gave us a hand with Kenny,' remarks Luke pointedly, meaning that Dan didn't. On another table, across the dining room, I hear Dougie's mum say to him, 'Are you sure it's a good idea to go round preaching when you get out of here, son?' There's some sniggering from Luke and Eric and shortly afterwards she and his other visitors leave. Sidney takes their place. He rubs his stubbly scalp and grins at us. Pete runs past and smacks him in the face. Sidney rocks back and then laughs at us. Pete comes back. He is hitting himself full-blown punches in the face, making himself stagger every time one lands. 'Go and sit him down for us, Buster,' Dan tells me. When I go over to him Pete squares up to me. 'Watch yourself with that skinny bastard,' Eric advises.

I'm pretty unhappy to be trying to restrain Pete's movements anyway. It's not fear, not in his case, it's just that it's unnecessary. What will be achieved if we sit him down? I obey orders and approach him. He swings at me and misses, then darts down towards the toilets and I follow him. Down here it's not so bad. The others aren't watching me so the pressure is less. 'Come on Pete, take it easy, I'm not going to hurt you,' I assure him softly. 'Super Sid, Super Sid,' Pete shouts. He is trapped down here and easy to contain until he quietens down. But I don't want to trap him. When he walks towards me I fall into step with him.

Back on the dormitory Eric is coming towards us. The others have not finished their tea yet. 'Get in there, you cunt,' Eric says, pushing Pete towards the toilets. Pete kicks out at Eric, who stinks of drink, but misses. I get hold of Pete to stop things getting worse. As I'm restraining him, Eric punches him three times on the side of the head. 'Behave yourself, you bastard,' he grunts, 'or you'll get some more of the same.' I'm stunned. I look to the others to see if they're watching. They are. But nobody says anything. Just to confuse me Pete immediately quietens down. Eric starts making a fuss of him and soon they're sitting together in the day room sharing a smoke.

Dan and I do the injections. Most of the patients need regular slow-release injections of tranquillizing drugs to keep them reasonably stable. 'Stable' is code for 'not causing any problems'. Brian and Dougie talk as we draw up Brian's Modecate. 'I was one of the Beatles, you know,' Dougie tells Brian. Dan looks at me and grins, as they can't see our faces. 'Oh yeah, which one were you?' Brian asks sarcastically. 'The fifth one,' says Dougie. 'But then I heard the call to preach and renounced my music.' This total divorce from reality is very hard for me to accept, even after three years in the job.

There's no ceremony involved with injecting these patients. Most of them get at least one a week. Dougie steps forward, drops his trousers and underpants and leans over with his hands on the bed. I stick the needle into the upper outer quadrant of his right buttock. There is still a spot plaster on his left buttock from the injection he had last week. As usual I seem to suffer more from giving the injection than the patient does who is receiving it. Probably I'm too soft for this carry-on altogether. Dougie chats on, talking rubbish, while I perspire freely and feel very uncomfortable pushing the plunger down on the viscous, oily tranquillizer. There are five to be done in total and Dan gets me to do them all. It's good practice, I suppose.

Billy wakes up and is much better, though very dry from all the drugs he's had pumped into him today. I make him some tea and toast as he missed his meals. He also has an apple. Dougie wanders across from his bed, which makes me wary because Dougie is really psychotic at the moment. That's what we call someone who sees rats everywhere they look and thinks, according to the conversation he had with his mother, that he's Jesus reborn and needs to go out preaching. He gives Billy a fag from a packet that should have been locked up in the office, and they sit chatting. Pete approaches and joins in. Billy, the Lord of the Cosmos and the New Messiah, draws deeply on the fag given him by Dougie, who's now decided he's the White Messiah and Jesus Reborn, while Pete, who is no kind of messiah at all, mumbles on about a 50-million-pound vase he's got hidden under a bush somewhere in the grounds. I keep thinking that there must be a basis for conflict here between these two messiahs. Jesus Reborn gives the Lord of the Cosmos a drink of lemonade and Pete a fag. I'm hoping nobody mentions Christmas and hang around just in case they do.

'You were late for work this morning!' Billy suddenly says to me. 'Er, yes, I was a bit late in,' I answer, watching his hands. I don't point out I'm on the afternoon shift. 'Yeah, you didn't get here until 9.30. Your wife told me you had slept in.' Dougie butts in: 'Does your wife work here?' 'Sort of,' I reply, not wanting to say no. Not to 'love' and 'hate' Billy Scott who might decide to give me a taste of both. 'What does she do?' Dougie asks. 'She's a nursery nurse,' I answer, not being quick enough to think of a lie.

I try to change the subject, which is getting decidedly sticky, and point to some tatty old flowers in a vase on a locker that a visitor must have brought in. 'They're nice flowers. I wonder what they are?' 'They're daffodils. They make herbs out of them,' says Billy. 'I thought daffodils were yellow,' answers Dougie. 'No they're not,' Billy retorts angrily. I try to change the subject again. 'I wonder what all that green stuff is around them; it gives a good effect.' 'They're rose hips,' Dougie answers quickly. 'They're not fucking rose hips, you daft cunt,' retorts Billy, with a flash of his earlier aggression. Dougie is momentarily diverted by a passing rat which he stamps on. 'Rose-hip jelly!' shouts Pete. I'm hoping nobody's going to make jelly out of me! 'I seem to remember collecting rose hips at school,' I say, getting desperate. 'We were always collecting something. Did you collect things at school, Dougie?' 'We collected conkers,' answers Dougie. 'And silver paper.' 'The silver paper went to Nyasaland because all the children were starving,' Billy informs us. 'I didn't know that,' says Dougie, interested. 'Yeah, they made silver coins out of it,' Billy says. 'Boodle,' says Pete with a momentary flash of interest.

Kenny comes back, having tapped a fag from somewhere, and goes and sits in the day room smoking it. Vernon explains to me about the key rings that the staff wear from their belts like jailers. Apparently it's their own private code to signify the adulterous among them. We agree it's a bit much. As we talk, Sidney walks up behind Kenny's chair. Quickly raising his hand he flings down a bunched fist upon the top of Kenny's head, as a man might strike a desk in anger. It's a hell of a blow and I'm half out my seat anticipating the explosion. Kenny just rubs his head, though, and says, 'Don't do that, Sidney.'

The TV blares on and from the games room comes the click of balls from the pool table. Dougie comes through and makes the other patients laugh chasing rats that aren't there but which he can see. Vernon goes to talk to him and calm him down. Brian walks through to the music room with a can of beer and soon the sounds of the telly are interwoven with the beat from the stereo. Pete runs in, sticks the nut on the psychopath, who is sitting quietly in his chair watching telly, and runs out again. I find myself on the psychopath's back as he tries to chase after Pete. 'All right, all right, take it easy,' I'm saying in his ear as he yells, 'I'll kill that bastard, I'll fucking kill him!' The others watch the telly as Vernon and Luke take off after Pete. He gets 100 milligrams of Largactil injected into his leg for his trouble. 'There will be nobody left up soon,' jokes Eric as we put Pete on our growing list of patients confined to bed. Not that he will stay there.

Sidney is sick everywhere. Poor, stubby-haired, totally bizarre Sidney. I clean him up, a disgusting mess of bile and regurgitated food. Halfway through, as I'm peeling off vomit-soaked clothes, he starts laughing at me. He howls as I struggle to pull his stinking trousers over his deformed feet. We laugh together, him laughing at me red-faced and struggling, me laughing at him laughing at me. It's a moment of unexpected fun in the course of the shift. Sidney goes to bed. I put the bed-cradle in to keep the weight of the blankets off his feet. He disappears completely under the covers. I go off with his dirty clothes and when I get back he's been sick all over his pillow and sheets so I have to start all over again.

The clock is moving slowly round to nine. One of the patients whose name I can't remember comes back from the pub stinking of drink. Eric slips out on some pretext for another crafty one himself. The drunk eats a bowl of cornflakes and talks sincere stupid talk to Dan about giving it up.

A phone call from a long-stay ward sends Luke off at top speed. One of the female nurses has been clobbered by a patient who's cut up rough. He brings him back a few minutes later and puts him in our seclusion room. The door isn't locked but he will stay there tonight and go back to his own ward tomorrow.

Dan takes a flier. 'I'm glad he's gone,' says Luke, getting his bag from his locker and going off to the clinical room. When he comes back it's bulging. The others laugh. 'Got the babies' shopping then,' Eric says. 'Fucking right I have,' answers Luke. 'Think I'm paying for the likes of cotton wool and Elastoplast when I can get it here for nowt.'

The night staff come in and Vernon makes the tea. I don't like the charge nurse on nights at all. He's already been sacked once and reinstated again. It's not just that, though. It's his manner. Big-headed, arrogant sod. He's one of those blokes who immediately gets up your nose.

Brian comes charging in. 'I know you,' he shouts at the young student nurse who's also on nights, 'going round telling everybody I'm a queer. Well I've had enough.' He's white-faced, sweating, pointing his finger straight at the lad's face. The lad looks sick with fear. 'I've not said anything, Brian . . .' he starts to say. 'Don't lie to me, you bastard. I heard you just now telling this lot I was a queer. Well you're going to get yours, you cunt.' Brian storms out. The charge nurse laughs at the student. 'I'm glad it's not me that's upset Brian,' he gloats.

The sense of relief as we leave is fantastic. By the time we hit the club I'm on a real high just to have survived the day without any major disasters. At the bar is Mr Neale, beside him a nursing auxiliary, a coat over her uniform, drinking heavily. There's the usual conflict between the outsiders wanting to play bingo and the workers coming in for a pint and a chat. Tonight they win and we go into the foyer, outside the toilets, which seems a fair reflection of our status as nurses within this institution. While

I'm standing there the nursing auxiliary comes out clutching a half-bottle of whisky and leaves. 'She must have finished work early to get drunk so quick,' I say. 'Don't be daft, soft lad,' says Luke. 'That's her starting work, not finishing!'

'I see that bastard Sebastian's off on the sick,' someone says. 'Good job if he stays off,' another voice adds. 'We can do without his kind here.' 'How can you say that?' Jack, a charge nurse, asks. 'It was that student who reported it, Maisie Campbell. The lad was only doing his job as a staff nurse. Anyway, who's to say she didn't see something.' 'Well I know who I'd believe,' says the voice. 'And it won't be some ginger-headed jockess backed up by a raving bender in a pink boiler-suit and ski-boots.' 'Oh, so just because you think he's a queer that makes him a liar, does it?' Jack asks. 'Maybe, maybe not, but if it's a toss-up between them two and Martin I know who my money is on. I've known Martin since he started here, and his dad before him.' 'That Sebastian wants his fucking face filling in,' added Luke. 'I'd give him a smack in the gob if I'd half a chance, the dirty grass!' 'Aye and that lass could do with a kick up the arse an' all,' adds another wise monkey.

The staff are like Mafiosi when it comes to things like this. Maisie and Sebastian, the staff nurse, have broken the unwritten code and reported Martin. The fact that the staff nurse is reputed to be gay doesn't help and I know his future here is over. I worry about Maisie and wonder if she's strong enough to weather the storm: all the little bits of sniping like that from Joy and Florrie; the backs turned on her in the club; people leaving rooms when she goes into them; the snide innuendos; threats on the phone. I know what the score is. I've seen it all before. There are staff here who haven't spoken to each other for 20 years for the same reason: reporting the abuse of patients. It brings into sharp focus Eric thumping Pete. I'd done nothing. A complaint would have finished me on the wards and nobody would be standing here drinking with me. Whether Maisie was right or not, I have to admire her pluck. Maisie. Strange to think of her as stronger than me, when for years I've looked on her like some sort of mad niece in need of frequent guidance. 'Well if Martin gets the boot, I can promise you that bastard will get my boot,' Luke says to general murmurs of agreement. Jack goes off early and looks pretty disgusted with the lot of them. I stay and get pissed.

Christmas Eve

I'm delegated to go out with one of the community psychiatric nurses, Joe, who is expecting a difficult time from a male patient. Luckily, before we can go out to visit the patient he's admitted to the disturbed ward via the police. 'May as well come out with me anyway,' says the dapper Joe. 'You can always dig us out if I get stuck.'

There's not really a lot we can do. The main road is open but the side roads are all pretty bad, even in town, and there's no question of going out into the country. We just go to visit those patients we think there is a chance of reaching.

The first is a dementing old lady. There is no response to our persistent ringing. We go next door where the neighbour is peering at us from the window. When we explain our business she lets us borrow her spare key.

Inside the front door is what was once a very nice home with unopened Christmas cards lying in a pile on the hall table. I'm amazed to recognize a photograph on the wall which turns out to be of a moderately famous daughter in the entertainment world. The old lady appears from the front room and smiles at us, never asking us our names or how we got into the house or what we are doing there. Joe introduces both of us and explains who we are, as she obviously doesn't remember him from his last visit. Her name is Mrs Cross. She is wearing a pot-pourri of clothing; nothing matches and all of it is filthy. Judging by her hands she has been getting in coal for the fire.

We follow Mrs Cross into the dining room. As she walks across the carpet in front of me she leaves large footprints. For a second I don't understand why this should be, then I realize it's dust.

Dust probably half an inch deep all over the room, which her footsteps displace, leaving a clear print. 'I'm having a bit of trouble lighting the fire,' she tells Joe hesitantly in a cultured voice. We investigate. The ash is baked solid under the grate and has not been cleared for months. The grate itself is full of ash and cinders on top of which is folded a whole newspaper. On top of this is the new coal. The house is freezing.

Joe has strategies for investigating houses. He asks if he can use the toilet and, receiving a positive answer, disappears upstairs where I hear him having a good look round. The toilet flushes several times but Mrs Cross pays no attention. Meanwhile I've started to clear the fire grate and it doesn't take as long as I thought it would to get a fire going. Joe comes back down while I'm doing this and gets the old lady to go with him into the kitchen, ostensibly to make a cup of tea but in reality to check her supplies of food.

When I finish with the fire I follow them into the kitchen. Mrs Cross is standing, oblivious of our presence, rubbing at a corner of a gas cooker on which the front ring is lit but no kettle has been placed. Joe indicates I should look in the cupboards. Most of them are empty but one or two contain bits and pieces that are hard to recognize. There is a sludge of meat, stinking and still in the paper the butcher wrapped it in. I throw it out. Milk bottles half full of green mould follow it. Joe helps the old lady with the tea and I look in the fridge for fresh milk, which there is, no doubt brought to the door by the milkman. The other thing about the fridge is that all the plastic interior is melted and charred. We work out, helped by some stumbling conversation from the old lady, that she has been defrosting it. When we ask her what with she indicates the gas poker she uses to light the fire!

The house is filthy. Curtains are black. We cannot see through the windows. The old lady looks ill and pale. There are many valuable objects under all the dust. Joe tells me she has been robbed several times. He doubts whether she will be admitted to the hospital. He's tried several times before without success. There's a shortage of places and people worse off than her.

Nevertheless he will ask the consultant to come and see her one more time. As we drive away, leaving her to a grey, crawling, fragile existence, Joe tells me the airing cupboard was full of neatly wrapped parcels of faeces which he's flushed away.

At the nursery for deprived children run by Social Services the roof is falling down. It is being temporarily supported by some metal props which have been decorated with paper streamers and balloons by the children and staff, to make them look less obtrusive. Joe is here to ask about the child of one of his female patients. A lady helping to look after the kids points her out. She sits alone, pale-faced, a dark shadow that could be a bruise on her forehead. I'm caught by her stillness and the lady tells me she does not join in with the games very much, if at all.

The nursery makes me feel a bit like Gulliver, everything is so small. Infant-sized chairs that don't reach my knee, toilet cubicles that don't reach my chest, little cots, the size of orange boxes, in rows for the afternoon siesta. In the main play area is a babbling sea of noise and colour and activity. Rough-and-tumble play the psychologists call it. To me it seems like bedlam. They slide and climb and scream and hit and fight and cry and generally have a great time.

We go to see the mother of the child. She lives around the corner. The housing estate is awash with children off from school for the Christmas holiday. They are bigger versions of the nursery kids and their fighting is more vicious and directed. As we stop outside the house a group of eight-year-olds are putting the boot in to one of their number. They scatter, thinking us to be the law in our collars and ties. We pick their crying victim out of the snow, brush him down and send him on his way.

The husband is in prison. On an old battered settee, leaning against a wall and reaching nearly to the ceiling, is the biggest pile of ironing I have ever seen in my life. It's hard to believe it's all hers but it appears there are six or seven kids on the scene so it's possible. A youngish child, a dog about to pup and a cat are also in the room. The inevitable television is going full blast. We sit down and have an instant coffee. She keeps working. Joe talks to her, I talk to the child and listen to them. She needs this visit, a sort of safety valve, a chance to unburden herself to somebody who seems to be interested in her and her problems. The child shows me his toys, getting them out of an understairs cupboard that is itself filled with more ironing, and tells me what Santa is going to bring him for Christmas. Hearing the long and improbable list being recited by her child the mother snorts. 'You've no chance, mate,' she tells him. The child gives me a crushed smile. On the TV the adverts show an endless stream of middle-class kids having fun with their expensive new toys.

The last call of the morning is to a retired insurance broker called Lionel who wears a collar and tie beneath his cardigan. The contrast between his opulent surroundings and our last visit couldn't be more emphatic. I wonder if his wife, a mean-faced woman, would even let us in the house if she knew where we had been sitting half an hour ago. The problems, however, are just as real. A bad case of agitated depression brought about by not preparing properly for retirement. The classic situation. A man of status and importance on the Friday. On the following Monday a nobody, a has-been. Always been too busy for hobbies, a bit too aloof for comradeship on the fairway or bowling green. Now he's left with a great big hole to fill, every day, and he doesn't know how. He's been over the garden so many times it's perfect and his wife doesn't want him under her feet in the house. All he's left with is a great yawning vacuum where once was work, and a galloping anxiety about how he's ever going to fill it. It doesn't help that he's addicted to Valium.

Joe is very skilled at what he does. It takes me some time to realize this because I'm not used to working with people with real therapeutic skills. Community psychiatric nurses like him can put as much or as little into the job as they like. He could run round jabbing needles into everybody and leave it at that. Nobody would say anything to him. The only real checks on his performance relate to whether he is fiddling his car expenses or not, the hospital being more concerned over the cost of its service than the quality.

Luckily for Joe's patients he's providing quality. We go over an anxiety management programme with Lionel that is already up and running, and set up another programme involving practical measures he can take to help fill his day. Some of these sound simple, like going out for a walk, but people in extremes of anxiety need help to think rationally, to see the obvious. Joe provides that help. He tries to get the wife involved therapeutically by doing simple things like rewarding Lionel with a bit of praise. She won't even come and talk to us about it, refuses to accept that Lionel needs anything more than to 'pull himself together', to 'give himself a shake'. Joe sets himself an objective to get her actively involved in Lionel's programme within the next four weeks.

After lunch in the local curry house Joe decides he's not making the best use of his time as we slip and slither along, getting nowhere fast. We head back to the hospital, making one last call along the way. Joe says it will be good experience for me and warns me what to expect.

The front door is opened by a pasty-faced, wasted-looking man, in the dirtiest shirt I have ever seen in my life. It's a good-quality shirt but about three sizes too big for him and absolutely filthy. Joe shakes hands and I follow him inside. We step into a horror story. The first thing is the smell. I don't retch, but it's a close call, saved by Joe's prior warning about conditions there. It's a smell I know well of urine and faeces, supercharged into a solid stinking wall by a blazing coal fire and the tightness of the surroundings. There is so much ammonia in the atmosphere from the urine that it makes my eyes smart and my breath catches in my throat.

I stand just inside the door on some bare floorboards left at the edge of the carpet. I don't really want to go any further into the room. It's difficult to take in details when everything is so appalling. The first thing that comes into focus are the yapping dogs. One of them, obviously excited by our presence, runs over and cocks his leg against a chair in the corner of the room. Neither Fred nor Pam, the occupants of the house, raises an eyebrow. When Joe introduces me I step forward to shake hands with Fred. Pam doesn't bother. My feet leave the bare floorboards with a loud slurp. Looking down I see the boards are soaked in pee and covered in trodden-in excrement, to which my feet have stuck.

As I start to be able to breathe again and my eyes stop running I look around more closely. Fred is giving Joe some papers to sort out for him, it seems the social workers won't call here! For once I can't blame them. Pam is lying on an old bed-settee adjacent to the fire. Piled around it are heaps of old cider bottles. The fire is unbelievably hot and banked right up the back of the chimney. On all the walls, but concentrated around the hearth, are great black stains. They puzzle me until Fred throws more coal on the fire with his bare hands and then wipes them on the wallpaper.

Pam looks at me with frank sexual interest and my flesh creeps. She wears a coat over a child's dress over an overall; all are filthy. She has long and disgustingly blackened nails on both hands and feet and a pair of cheap, dirty white shoes lie on the floor near her. Her tights are full of holes, her longish hair looks like it's been washed in chip fat. I know Pam from when she was an in-patient at the hospital, provider of sexual favours to fellow patients behind the church, at a cost of two Woodbines. She looks as if she has a tan but it's ground-in dirt.

Fred leads the way into the kitchen at Joe's request. A dustbin sits in the middle of the kitchen floor. 'Don't you think it might be a bit more hygienic if that was outside?' Joe asks. 'Don't be fucking daft, man,' says Fred. 'They'd nick all our fucking coal.' Lifting the lid reveals a dustbin full of coal. 'Where do you put your rubbish?' Joe asks, looking across Fred, at me, with uplifted eyebrows. 'Throw it on the fucking garden,' Fred chortles. We move across to the old stone sink, which is stained and repulsive. Next to it is a fridge, the large old type that you see on 1950s films. The fridge is surprisingly well stocked with bacon and eggs and we don't enquire too closely where they have come from.

In the bathroom the bath is inaccessible because of the old-fashioned push-pull lawn mower parked inside the door. Not that the bath would be much use to anyone, it's full of dirty clothes. Fred pops into the toilet for a pee and Joe tells me about the clothes. Fred and Pam never buy any, instead the local rag-and-bone man keeps them supplied in return for a go at Pam whenever he feels like it. 'I tried to get them to wash some clothes once,' Joe recounts. 'We put them in the bath to soak while I was here, then Pam was going to take them out to wash and dry them later. After a month I gave up and took them out myself. By the way,' he adds as an afterthought, 'don't sit down, whatever you do, Pam's urinated on most of the chairs and any she's missed the dogs have got.'

To go upstairs we have to go back through the sitting room. Fred stops to take a drink from a large pint mug on top of the mantelpiece. It's the dirtiest object I've ever seen in my life. As we traverse the rooms one of the over-excited dogs is having a crap in the corner. 'Come on, Fred,' Joe tells him. 'You can't just let them carry on like this, you know! Get something and clear it up.' 'Oh don't worry about that lot,' Fred assures us, 'I'll chuck it out on the garden later.' Joe insists and Fred eventually gives in and chucks it out on the garden now. He does this by opening the front door, getting the coal shovel and scooping the offending article outside. Joe looks at me and raises his eyebrows heavenwards. No wonder the neighbours are always complaining.

We go upstairs behind Fred to a scene far worse than downstairs. The first door he opens reveals an empty room. Empty of furniture, that is. On the floor is a solid layer of onion skins and against the far wall another huge pile of clothing, obviously from the rag-and-bone man. I laugh, I just can't help it. Joe shakes his head without saying a word. Fred starts to explain but Joe is already moving on to the next room, leaving him behind.

There is a bed with no sheets, covered only by filthy, urine-soaked blankets; a green pillow, the colour of which can only be discerned at the edges as it's so black; and a mattress that looks as if somebody's stripped a car engine on it. Beside the bed is a broken-down red plastic bucket full of urine, in which float old cigarette ends and toffee papers. Joe looks at the bucket. 'Another of my failures,' he explains philosophically. 'Pam kept wetting the bed because the toilet's downstairs and she was too lazy to get up and go to it. The hospital wouldn't give me a commode for her so I bought the bucket in the hope she would use that instead. It was great for a few days, the only trouble was that she was also too lazy to empty the bucket! As soon as it filled up she left it and started wetting the bed again. Now and then Fred comes in drunk and knocks it over, then she starts using it again.' In the whole house, this Christmas Eve day, there is not one single thing which would remind you of tomorrow.

Back out in the car, Joe turns to me with his usual friendly grin. 'What did you think to that, then?' he asks. 'My skin's crawling,' I answer, wanting to scratch hard at myself. He chuckles. 'You get used to it,' he says. 'I've seen worse than that.' 'Impossible!' I exclaim emphatically. 'Nothing, but nothing, could be as bad as that.' Joe's smiling again. 'Listen,' he says, 'I had to go and see a guy once who'd held up the local shop with a cricket bat and stolen a can of prunes. His house was one of those big old detached efforts but there wasn't a pane of glass left in it, the local kids had smashed them all. Instead, every window was sheeted over with cardboard from old boxes to keep the rain out. There was no electric or gas so I stumbled about inside using my cigarette lighter to see where I was going. The front room was three feet deep in rubbish! The guy never threw anything out in case it came in useful! In the middle of all this were a few cardboard boxes full of earth with some pale old dandelions growing in them. "What's that?" I asked him. "That's me sunken garden," he answered, as if it was perfectly normal. All around the room were these huge fungi growing out the walls because it was so damp and musty.' 'Oh come on,' I say, 'you're having me on.' Joe's got the car going now but he keeps talking. 'There were no doors, he'd burnt them all on the fire to keep warm and the kitchen was even worse than the living room. Upstairs was a bedroom with one of those old high beds with the springs. There wasn't a mattress or anything else to lie on, just a dirty old blanket to cover him. I went round the other rooms, they were carpeted wall to wall with milk cartons full of pee. When I looked at the toilet it was blocked up with old faeces. 'What do you do about that?' I asked him. "I shit on the shovel and then burn it on the fire," he said, as if it was a dead normal thing to do. You haven't seen anything yet.'

We drive back to the hospital as it's still too early to knock off for the day. There's a multi-disciplinary meeting on the male disturbed ward which Joe is going to, so I tag along. The meeting, as usual, is a bit of a non-event but Dan, the charge nurse, collars me in his office after it. 'Any chance of you giving us a hand tonight at our party, Buster?' he asks. 'I wouldn't ask, not on Christmas Eve, but with this weather I can't see many of my own lads actually being able to get here.' I don't want the aggro I'll get if I turn him down but I certainly don't want to spend Christmas Eve in this dump. 'I'd never get my time back for coming in,' I point out, 'I've no more time to do on this ward.' He picks up the phone and asks for the nursing officer. There's a brief conversation about me and then Dan puts the phone down again. 'OK, I've managed to get you paid overtime,' he says, as if he's done me a big favour. Anne's working a late anyway so I make the best out of a bad job and put a brave face on it. 'Oh, that's all right then. I'll see you later on.' Joe thinks it's funny when I tell him and says I should be more assertive. I tell him bollocks. Probably because he's right.

I'm left with the problem of killing the rest of the afternoon, as Joe's got nothing else for me to do and it's not worth while going all the way home in the snow just to come back again. I decide to go to the acute wards' Occupational Therapy Department and pick up a project I'd done while working there. When I pass the bus stop there is a lady on the bus trying to say something through the window to a male patient in his thirties, her son I guess, who is standing outside in the snow. You can see he doesn't want her to go and she looks guilty at leaving him. There is something about her nice rouged face, herringbone coat and plastic gloves with a split at one knuckle that catches the sadness of visiting relatives, who always seem at a loss to understand the behaviour of those they love. I phone Anne and tell her what I'm doing. She seems to find it hard to understand my behaviour!

When I get to Therapies the place is in gales of laughter.

Pushing through the crowd I find that the students are putting on a Christmas show which is an undisguised piss-take of the hospital with lots of 'Doctor Doctor' jokes and plenty of laughs at the expense of the system. The patients love it though I doubt if Mr Neale would appreciate the beer-swilling, fag-smoking caricature of him which is being presented on the improvised stage.

The project I've come to pick up relates to the bird-spotting club I'd started, which we'd had a lot of fun with. Tim was a great fan of the club but tended to get sidetracked all the time. He would freak out, looking at the world through a pair of binoculars, and forget that he was supposed to be identifying birds, concentrating instead on blades of grass or ants or almost anything else that caught his eye. I didn't mind. He was outside, getting some fresh air, and he was happy. I'd watch him sometimes, leaning back so far you couldn't believe he wouldn't fall over, peering through the binoculars he held with one hand while the other waved excitedly about his head. It was great to see someone enjoying themselves in this place. Melody was a different kettle of fish. I started to realize that whenever we got into a particularly dark piece of undergrowth Melody was there beside me! Then the letters started arriving. It came to a head one day when she slipped into the staff-room behind me. It was all really sticky. I didn't know how to deal with it. She was a great girl, attractive and intelligent, but that wasn't the point – this was supposed to be a nurse–patient relationship. Melody just didn't see it like that. She persisted and I suppose I panicked, being alone with her and all, and was too rough on her feelings. I was trying to get her out of the room quickly before anybody saw her and added one and one together to make four. She got upset, pinched the staff nurse's scooter and pissed off on it. What a day that had been. I didn't want another like it.

After we'd finished our fieldwork we used to find photographs of the birds, or paint pictures of them ourselves, to stick on a tree we'd made. I asked Tim to paint some snow on the tree and when I came back every bit of it was covered in white dots! Tim also painted us a crow that looked as if it had flown into a brick wall, but I was delighted for him. Melody was a natural artist. It used to cut me up to see all that beauty and talent festering away in a place like this. Drawing birds for my tree when by rights she should have been painting pictures to hang in galleries.

After I've had a cup of tea with the OT girls and discussed my project with their boss, who gives me a good mark for it, Tim corners me for a chat. He's much better today and we have a good laugh together. He's got such a good sense of humour. When the snow starts falling again, a real blizzard this time, he points out of the window with a serious face saying, 'The Snowmen are coming.' Then he's so slayed by his own wit that he goes rolling off around the room, bent double with laughter, tears rolling down his face, with me in the chair creased up in the same condition.

The last session of the day is the inevitable bingo, which the patients love because the first prize is always a packet of fags. The main OT room is packed but nobody will volunteer to do the calling because that cuts them out of the prizes. Tim, who had wandered off somewhere, comes back in and promptly takes the job on. 'All the steps, thirty-nine,' he shouts. 'Two chubby checkers, eighty-eight. Ten more steps, forty-nine. Twenty-one, key to the door, not eighteen in this case.' He starts laughing at his own wit again and I'm getting nearly hysterical myself by this stage. The crowd don't appreciate it. 'Tell him to do it right, the silly idiot,' one of the patients barracks. Tim continues laughing, oblivious to their concerns. 'Number ninety, all the way. Sixty-nine, too old to cry ninety. Eleven, old enough to eat eggs. Ten, the end of your schooldays. Seventy-five, time you died. Sixty-four, nearly time to retire, sixty-four. By the way' – a long pause follows – 'has anybody got anything yet?' This is too much for the crowd, who have been getting increasingly restive. 'Do it properly,' and similar cries erupt from around the room. 'Four and one, forty-one; the other way round, fourteen,' Tim continues, enjoying himself immensely. Two people shout for a line, one coming up on fourteen and one coming up on forty-one. Mayhem ensues, which gets worse when the players realize Tim hasn't been recording which numbers he's called out, so the cards can't be checked. A riot is avoided by the OT helper stepping in to take over and me taking Tim off for another drink of tea. He's laughing fit to burst.

I wander back towards the ward with him, killing time and enjoying his company. It's always quieter in the afternoons on Acutes, with a lot of patients away at Therapies. Two policemen in uniform pass me in the corridor and I start to notice it's too quiet. Nikki comes out of the office. 'I brought Tim back,' I explain. 'He was about to get lynched by the bingo crowd.' Tim, who is standing beside me, thinks this is hilarious and staggers away choking with laughter. 'Got the police in then?' She follows my eyes down the corridor to the departing officers. 'We've had a suicide,' she sighs, then looks directly at me. 'Emma Jane's drowned herself.' I feel the shock pass physically through my body followed by waves of goose bumps and a cold sweat. 'Put the kettle on,' she says, walking off, thinking because I'm upset I haven't noticed how upset she is.

Over tea she tells me about it. 'She got off the ward this morning, nothing to stop her, she wasn't on constant observation any more. We didn't even miss her till lunchtime, just thought she was in her room as usual.' Nikki lights a cigarette and crosses her long, shapely legs. 'When Liam realized she'd gone we had a good look round for her but in this lot . . .' She waves her hand at the window and the snow beyond, leaving a line of smoke. Nikki inhales again, deeply. 'She was in the fishpond, face down in four inches of water. She'd broken the ice to do it.' Nikki looks across at me: 'Buster, Emma Jane must have forced her face under the water and held it there.' She looks really dejected and I start to understand the need for black boots, mini-skirts, a good time. Anything to blot this lot out of your mind for an hour or two. Which is what I'm going to have to learn to do. I feel as if I should cry or something but I can't.

I have something to eat in the hospital canteen and then go up to the Nurses' Home to kill the hour still remaining before the party. The TV room has a few people in it, but nobody I'm friendly with, so I go upstairs to the corridor off which the rest of my group live. Maisie, Joanna and Rosemary are moping about in the kitchen when I get there. Depression isn't the name for it. 'Christmas Eve,' wails Rosemary. 'Christmas Eve and I'm stuck here. I don't believe it.' Even the normally ebullient Maisie looks somewhat downcast. 'Any chance of a shag?' she asks me. 'I need something to cheer me up!' Joanna laughs. 'Maisie,' she reprimands her, 'you can't just say things like that.' 'Why not?' asks Maisie, unrepentant. 'Ah well, if I cannae have a shag at least put the kettle on.' I do as she requests and put the kettle on.

Rosemary is looking particularly cheesed off. 'My mother's bought a massive turkey for Christmas dinner, the whole family will be there, even my brother's home on leave. How come every time it snows the whole country grinds to a halt? You just can't get anywhere at all,' she complains. 'My mum couldn't get down from the farm to do her Christmas shopping,' Joanna chips in, 'but she's plenty of food in the freezer so at least they can eat. They're used to getting cut off in the winter.' 'Well I'm bloody well not,' Maisie says. 'Just think of all that grub going to waste at home and me sitting here starving,' Rosemary groans. 'You'll no starve, you big lump,' Maisie tells her, but Rosemary is unconvinced. 'Why don't you all come round to ours for Christmas dinner?' I say. 'There's plenty to eat and at least you know you'll be able to get there. Besides, it'll be a change from this place.' The girls fall silent and look at one another, waiting for someone to take the lead. 'We can't do that,' Joanna says. 'Anne will have a fit if us lot turn up at the door.' 'Shush,' says Maisie, uninhibited by such considerations, 'who says we cannae. I'll come, Buster.' A general row ensues, at the end of which it's decided they're all coming but that they're all going to bring something to eat with them. I hand out the tea and try to think how to break the news to Anne.

'Oh no, here's the rozzers again,' says Joanna from her seat by the window. Rosemary jumps to her feet and peers out. 'It's those same two that were here before,' she says. 'I wonder what they're after this time?' We soon find out. 'But how come it's my room you want to search first?' Rosemary protests. 'How come it was me that was getting asked all the questions last time you were here?' 'Come along, Miss,' says the bigger of the two men, and they're both pretty big, 'let's get it over with.' He turns to the rest of us. 'Do you all live here?' I point out I'm just visiting. He asks me a couple of questions and then tells me to clear off. 'I'll see you at the social,' Maisie says. 'I'll be the one in handcuffs.'

It's Vernon's do. Unfortunately Vernon's no good at organizing people or events – I mean to say, a social on Christmas Eve! We get stuck into it, clearing the day room for dancing and pushing the chairs back against the wall. The small tables we stick in the games room out of the way. The disco comes and looks pretty professional, run by a guy who works at the hospital, so we leave him to set up on his own. He knows the score. A couple of other staff arrive to help, having battled here through the weather. 'What a relief to get out of that pigging house for a couple of hours,' Luke says. 'She's driving me nuts getting things ready for tomorrow.'

Micky and I organize the drink. Micky is a rough diamond. He calls a spade a spade. There's a good rapport between him and the patients because he's like so many of them in his background. Often as not Micky will have gone to school with one or more of them. The rest of us are often caught out by not understanding the world they belong to: Micky does. He lives on the estate from which a lot of our patients come and maybe the guy he's nursing this week will be buying him a pint next week. Despite all the training the qualified staff on this ward have had between them, no matter how good it is, and it's generally pretty poor, not one of them can get on with the patients like Micky. The thing is, he likes playing endless games of snooker and reading the *Sun*. He doesn't have to act interested, he's genuine, and that's what the patients spot, sitting there with 24 hours a day to watch the staff and weigh them up. I often wonder what the ward would be like if he was running it.

The drink is prodigious. No spirits but plenty of beer, sherry, lager, Babycham and wine. We make a punch out of whatever we can find and Leo's Antabuse vodka appears from somewhere and goes in as well, though it's probably 90 per-cent water by now. Micky makes the punch and drinks lager. 'Get yourself a drink, bucko,' Micky says. 'You get fuck-all else for your trouble in this spot.' He's right, of course. Though the way he puts it makes me laugh, he has a way of hitting the nail on the head. The punch looks lethal by the time we're finished.

Some of the younger patients are pretty excited. It's a hell of a strain on them cooped up in here for most, or all, of the time. Tonight they know there are women coming and there's booze to be had. They keep sticking their heads round the door of the kitchen. 'Give us a drink, Micky, for fuck's sake,' they beg. Micky drinks his lager slowly from the can, slaps his lips together, wipes his mouth with the back of his hand. 'Ah, good drop of gear that, but not for you bastards.' It sounds bad but he's only kidding them on and they love it, groaning and going off back to the ward where they laugh with each other about 'that cunt Micky'.

Leo comes in rubbing his hands. He seems to have recovered from his Antabuse therapy and to be looking forward to the party. 'Want a hand, lads?' he asks. 'Aye, a hand to drink all this wallop, you mean, you crafty cunt Leo,' jokes Micky. 'And don't think you'll be giving that girlfriend of yours one on the sly either – I'm on bed patrol tonight so no hole for you, sunshine!' 'Eh, get off, Micky. What do you think I am?' Leo asks, looking innocent. 'I know what you are,' laughs Micky. 'You're a horny little get, so behave yourself.' Leo laughs and withdraws. 'Is his bird coming tonight?' I ask Micky. 'No, she's off her nut at the moment, but don't tell him that. He'll find out soon enough.' 'Is Brian still deluded about him?' I query. 'I'll say,' Micky answers cheerfully. 'He went for him at teatime but me and Eric sorted it out before he got into his stride. Can't have that sort of carry-on.' He doesn't explain how they sorted it out and I don't ask. 'Where is he now, in bed?' 'No, that daft sod let him out for a walk to cool off.' Micky indicates Dan, visible through the serving hatch. 'He'll cool off all right with ten pints of lager inside him. That's where he'll be now, down the pub getting pissed up.

I tell you that guy's dangerous; he'll top somebody one of these days. He damn near did for old Eric once, shaking him by the neck he was, like a rag doll.' Micky mimes to me what the unfortunate Eric looked like with Brian's strong hands wrapped around his neck. It seems Micky and I share our misgivings. The difference is that Micky, still flopping about like a puppet without strings, appears to know no fear.

Eventually the drink is sorted out and I go to the main kitchen to collect the food for the party. They've decided on pie-and-peas suppers, on Christmas Eve! We'll have to serve it up but at least it's all cooked and waiting in the heated trolley. 'Tell Eric I got some stuff for him,' the chef says, piling some trays of mince pies on top of the trolley. Eric the weasel, like his namesake, lives off the land around here and never needs to buy a thing. I promise to pass the message on and lumber off with the trolley. It's really a porter's job to do this but I'm extra and the porters are short-staffed like the rest of the hospital so I don't mind – they do us enough favours and that's a fact. All the staff are drinking hard in the ward kitchen when I get back.

Our guests begin to arrive, mostly accompanied by the nurses from their wards, and the place soon fills up. I'm standing having a drink and talking to Micky when one of the general nursing students, who have to come here for their psychiatric experience, leaves her group of elderly female patients and comes across to speak to me. She's one of that freshly scrubbed type of student, all teeth and enthusiasm. 'I know you,' she says, 'but I bet you don't know me.' Micky's listening, all ears for a bit of scandal. I take a good look at her but I can't remember ever having seen her before in my life. 'Sorry,' I say with a shrug of my shoulders, 'the face doesn't ring a bell.' 'I'm not surprised,' she laughs. 'I was working in Theatres the day you came in to have your vasectomy!' Beside me there's a huge guffaw and Micky's spraying his beer all over the room trying not to choke on it. 'Thanks a bundle,' I think to myself as yet another story sets off along the hospital grapevine.

There's not much dancing to begin with because it's mostly the older women that arrive first. They know there's some grub and booze on the go and that's all they are interested in. One of them even asks when we are dishing out the food and then goes off to play bingo on another ward until it's time. They can be a pretty fly bunch all right. Our younger male patients and one horny older man start getting the female nurses from the other wards up to dance. Some patients arrive off the female disturbed ward with Maisie in tow. 'What happened with the coppers?' I ask her. 'Nothing,' she answers. 'Turned the whole place upside down and found nothing. Rosemary's fuming, says she's going to complain to the Race Relations Board because she's being discriminated against. I think she's right, she's getting picked on.' 'How about you?' I ask her, changing the subject. 'Are you still getting picked on?' She shrugs her shoulders. Micky makes a point of coming across to speak to her, which really surprises me, and once again I notice the staff are using Maisie's case to make a statement about where they stand.

Before you know it the disco is going full blast. One of the disturbed ward girls is really on heat and nearly rapes the old bloke on the dance floor, much to the amusement of the other male patients. Then she starts doing the same for everyone, even coming across to get Micky up for a dance. Once she gets him on the floor it's like a wrestling match, her hands are all over him. Micky's laughing like crazy when he eventually gets away from her. 'Fuck me, I've been raped,' he gasps, coming back where the staff stand drinking in their own small group, 'She's really got a problem.'

> 'Old MacDonald had a farm,
> E I E I O.
> And on that farm he had some bulls,
> E I E I O.
> And the bulls were bulling it here,
> And the bulls were bulling it there,
> They were bulling it here,
> Bulling it there,
> Bulling it everywhere.
> Old MacDonald had a farm,
> E I E I O.'

I can't remember how it starts, it just seems to be one of those things that develops for no reason. All I know is that I'm in the middle of the floor doing the dirty version of 'Old MacDonald's Farm' with Maisie and two or three other willing souls, one of whom is just pretending to ravish me from the back, in true bull fashion, before we turn around and I return the compliment. The roar of laughter is deafening and among the audience I see wholesale 'bulling' breaking out as the younger patients join in the fun. The older ones don't know whether to hold on to their false teeth or their sides as they gasp with laughter at the rare sight of the staff deliberately making fools of themselves.

The party's going really well, and breaking off to dish out the pie and peas hardly interrupts things at all. The drink is on a tight rein because most of the patients just knock it back until they're sick. We've also got Leo and a couple of other characters with drink problems and have to be careful they're not getting the others to supply them with booze. In the kitchen we're sweating, dishing out the food and drink and helping ourselves to a few more cans as well. Some relatives turn up with more ale and some crisps and stuff, so that, all in all, it's turning into a really terrific evening, easily the best social I've seen in the hospital. Which is one up to Vernon. That's when Brian arrives back from the pub.

I see Maisie making pleading faces at me where I'm working in the kitchen. I think she's joking and grimace back at her. The fact that she's in trouble doesn't register until I hear Brian's raised voice. By the time I'm through the door Luke has already jumped in and the two of them are rolling about on the floor, arms locked around each other. Tables full of pie-and-peas suppers are scattered to the four corners of the room as I dive in just ahead of Micky, grab an arm and hold on to it. In the confusion somebody takes the opportunity to boot me in the back, It's quite a battle to overpower Brian but eventually we get the better of him.

Dan compounds his earlier mistake and lets Brian get up and go into the dormitory to cool off. A few minutes later and Brian's at it again, shouting and swearing. 'Where's that cunt? I'm going to fucking kill him, calling me a queer.' Dan talks to him. 'Calm down Brian, nobody's talking about you and I don't want you spoiling everybody's fun.' But Brian's as deluded as hell, nearly in tears. 'How would you like to be called a fucking poof?' he shouts, though nobody had called him that. 'It's not right. I'm going to have him.'

We talk and cajole and bribe, trying to keep the evening going and not let this big get spoil it. Brian starts stalking about through the revellers though, and that's that. Those big solid footsteps, the white perspiring face, the fixed stare, always at Leo, on whom his delusion seems to centre. 'Go and tell him on the disco to wind it up, Buster,' Luke tells me. 'We'll try and clear the place a bit before he starts.' I go to the disco and then round all the small knots of nurses, telling them what's happening. They don't need a second warning and some of the old hands have already cleared off. I'm just explaining to a young student who has only been working in the hospital a week when the whole thing blows up.

Leo's standing near me, talking to a young female patient, when Brian comes stamping across the room like a runaway train. Leo has the sense to duck behind me and for the second time that week I'm in the wrong place when Brian's about to blow his top.

I start to say something, but Brian has had enough of talking, he half drops his hands and then up they come again. The first punch whistles past my ear as I dodge sideways to avoid it. Two more follow, one catching me in the guts and the other in the side of the head, and then Micky lands on his back, getting an arm wrapped round his neck and one round his head. I grab a hold, but it's like snatching at a bucking bronco and I'm so winded by the belt in the stomach that I can hardly keep a grip of him. We spin around and around in a heaving mass. Maisie comes flying in but bounces off as if she'd hit a revolving door, and then the other staff slam into us and we topple slowly over, crashing on to some patients sitting in chairs, rolling over the top of them like a steam-roller. I'm holding on for grim death and end up crushed on the bottom of the pile, my face tight up against Brian's, who's right on top of me. For a few long seconds we're trapped eyeball to eyeball, Brian trying to get his teeth into my nose and me trying to stop him, then the human snowball rolls off me and I can breathe again.

'Get his legs,' somebody shouts, as more male reinforcements arrive from other wards and, with eight of us holding him, we eventually manage to get his feet off the ground and bear him away through the ward to the seclusion room, putting him down on the mattress and sitting on him there. I kneel on one arm, Luke on the other, with Micky on his legs. 'You fucking bastards,' Brian shouts as he struggles, 'I'll fucking kill you all.' We hold on until he quietens down a bit. 'Are you going to behave?' Luke asks. 'Or am I to get the doctor up to you?' Brian lunges at him with his head and Luke has to jerk backwards to avoid being butted in the face. 'Right, get his fucking clothes off,' Luke instructs. 'No cunt's mucking me about like this.' He proceeds to jerk Brian's Tee-shirt over his head, tearing it in the process. 'Where the fuck do you think you are?' Luke shouts at Brian. 'Eh, what the fuck do you think you're up to?' We strip Brian to his underpants. The seclusion room is stifling with all the people in it and the adrenalin flowing through us. Dan sends for the doctor. 'Everybody all right?' Luke asks, calming himself down.

The doctor comes, a little black man, and tries to talk to Brian as we hold him down. 'Fuck off, you black bastard! No fucking Paki's touching me.' Brian obviously isn't impressed with the line of reasoning being followed. We roll him over and Dan sticks a needle in his backside, giving him some haloperidol to calm him down. Then, using a controlled release, we shut the door on him and put the seclusion policy into operation. I'm relieved to see the locks turned.

The party is over when we come out. Only a few stragglers are still waiting to disperse. The girl with the hots has turned aggressive, so Micky and I help Maisie walk her back to the female disturbed ward. Then we go back and take stock of ourselves. Three of us have casualty forms to fill in, plus one for Brian. We sit round in the office drinking beer out of cans and filling out the forms. In a way it was lucky there had been a social, as even with the extra staff on duty we were hardly able to deal with Brian. The normal afternoon staffing level is only three people. Eric arrives back from the hospital Social Club where he's avoided all the trouble. Leo comes back soaked to the skin, absolutely dripping wet. 'Where the fuck have you been?' Dan asks, exasperated at Leo's bedraggled condition. Leo grins, snow in his hair. 'The dirty little bastard's been getting his end away,' Micky butts in with a grin, summing it all up in his own inimitable style.

I get a lift into town and stop off at the Lantern for a pint. It's got a bit of a reputation, this place. I don't suppose there's many pubs where they have the chairs screwed to the floor. Playing football for them, I have no problems drinking here. The best thing about the place is that you don't usually see anybody from the hospital in here. Patients or staff. Or that's what I thought. I've just managed to get myself a seat among the revellers, enjoying the first inch of a really good beer, when Sebastian plonks himself down next to me. The juke box has been topped up with all the old Christmas records and John Lennon is singing the best of them. 'How are you?' I ask him, thanking my lucky stars he isn't wearing the pink boiler-suit, looking round with an apologetic smile at the people I know – some of whom grin back at me. Not that there's any need to ask, he looks terrible. 'You know what's going on?' he asks. I nod my head. 'The bastards,' he says quietly but with a disturbing intensity. 'They ring me up at home, they write letters to my house, all of them threatening what's going to happen. I don't know what to do.' He sits there looking really dejected. 'If I was you, Sebastian, I'd get off out of it,' I advise him. 'But I've just got settled into a new place,' he pleads. 'Why should I go? I haven't done anything wrong.' 'It's not worth it,' I tell him. 'You know what they're like, they'll never forgive you. Get out of it, make a fresh start, there's no future for you here any more.'

Suddenly the place is full of people from the hospital. I can't believe my eyes, there must be 30 or 40 of them piling in through the door. Sebastian sees them, gets up hurriedly and goes. A couple of them jeer him as he leaves. I stay to finish my drink. Some of them come over and sit down. It's the acute wards' Christmas pub-crawl. A few literally are – crawling, that is. Gloria sticks her arm around me and gives me a friendly squeeze that will probably leave bruises. 'Are you going to buy me a drink, Buster?' she slurs, trying to get her tongue into my ear. 'You don't want to be seen drinking with the likes of that toe-rag,' Sam says, referring to Sebastian. 'He's bad news, that bastard.' Suddenly I'm annoyed. It's not often I lose my temper but when I do it's like lighting a blue touch-paper. I find myself on my feet. 'I'll drink with who the f—' I start to say, when the wind is taken right out of my sails by the drunken Gloria leaning forward and unzipping my trousers. 'Going to show us your operation scars, Buster?' she yells, bringing forth a gale of laughter at my expense.

Christmas Day

The walk itself takes me 55 minutes. There are no buses today, no tyre marks yet to cut along the streets of snow. The frost is hard, the pavements and roads a sparkling white beneath the burning orange lamps.

Drawing nearer to the hospital, cars start to overtake me, windows steamed up from blowing heaters. Faces, white blobs, look out at me in passing, though no one stops to offer me a lift. A lonely stretch of moonlit road still lies ahead.

The hospital sails into view at the lane end, a river steamer ablaze with lights in the pre-dawn country darkness. Inside the Nursing Office the heat is stifling. The door of today's ward is locked, leaving me pacing about in the endless empty corridor until a passing staff nurse takes pity on a student and turns aside to let me in.

Upstairs I kiss the night nurse, who departs quickly. And then just me. Alone with 27 females in the slumbering night-light of the ward. Several of them sit in chairs lined up against the wall. The clock moves to 6.45, the calendar shows December 25th. It is the Year of Our Lord 1984. They will have been dressed for hours.

Josie comes and sits down in the office where I'm pouring out a cup of tea, the skin sagging now around her neck, in this her fortieth year of incarceration. Other ladies doze quietly around me. 'Can I have a cigarette please, Buster?' she asks my back. 'You know better than that, Josie,' I tell her without turning round. She takes no offence from my refusal. 'Do you fancy a cup of tea, Josie?' I ask her, already pouring it out, knowing that she never refuses. 'I'm going to tell you something, Buster,' Josie says, taking the tea, 'but you mustn't let any of these buggers hear.' She indicates the other ladies in the room and draws closer to me. 'That Anthea's been going with men for cigarettes . . .' she starts to say. I hold up my hand and shake my head. 'Now stop it, Josie. You can pack that tale-telling in before you start.' For a brief moment she pauses and then continues on a different, totally unrelated track. 'When I was born my mother had a terrible time, what with me being half mouse and half donkey.' This is a familiar theme of hers and I doze slightly as she rambles on in the dim shadowy office where the calendar marks another, equally complex, birth.

Sister comes in, except she doesn't like to be called Sister. 'Call me Moira,' she tells everyone. It's harder for the patients to do this than anybody else. 'Merry Christmas, Buster.' 'Merry Christmas, Moira.' We exchange kisses and greetings. Her lips are hot and moist. 'Why are there so many ladies up?' she queries. 'It's Christmas Day, for goodness sake!' She's great, Moira – still full of interest and enthusiasm after years at this job. The others probably won't even think it's odd that the patients are up, if they notice.

Martha comes in completely starkers! She's huge, all gut and swinging tits. 'Oh, can you help me with this please?' she asks in her la-di-da accent, waving her bra at me. Bra! It's more like a couple of buckets tied together with rope. Moira helps her fit it on, seeing me balk at the task. She blows on her hands first, to warm them, then wrestles each of Martha's enormous sagging breasts into her bra. 'Thank you very much, dear,' Martha says before wobbling off as bare-arsed as she arrived.

'Well, I'm not getting anybody up before eight o'clock today,' Moira informs me. 'Those who want to can have a lie-in. We'll do breakfasts just as and when the ladies come downstairs.' She crosses over and looks at the large desk diary. 'There's three of us on this morning,' she tells me, reading from the diary. 'Tracy, the student from the General, is on here as well. If she makes it.' The ward maid, they call her Rose, comes up for a cuppa, having prepared the breakfast tables downstairs. Moira tells her what we're going to do about breakfast and I can see by the thinning of the lips that the information would have been appreciated earlier. There's a lull in the conversation. Complete silence descends upon the manger-dark office, the ladies in here have all gone back to sleep. Josie's teeth are hanging out of her mouth as she snores gently in her chair.

Tracy arrives with a bad hangover. There's another pot of tea mashed for her and those patients sitting in with us. It's nice that we can all sit together like this; on most wards it would not be allowed. 'Shall we open our presents then?' asks Rose. There's a lot of laughter as we rake through the bran tub and get them out. A pair of red briefs and a half-bottle of whisky for me. Tracy blushes as she opens her parcel to find the frilly camisole and knickers I have bought her. A blush which turns fiery red when the wakening Josie, looking for all the world like an elderly relative, leans across and says, 'You want to watch some man doesn't try and get his meat into you with that lot on. They're a dirty lot of buggers!'

The crowd outside the night office has thickened. Every few minutes one of them comes and looks in at the door and then goes back and sits down. Always the same unasked question, 'When are we going downstairs?' Putting the pressure on us to conform to the routine they are addicted to after years of institutionalization. At eight o'clock we make a move. Moira unlocks the door that leads to the stairs and steps back from the charge. Nicotine starvation lies behind all this activity. Three of the older ladies come down in the lift with me and a bag of dirty laundry that nobody has picked up.

In the office Moira sits besieged at her desk. She has unlocked the cigarette drawer and is handing out various packets of fags and matches, each with a name written on it, to their owners. They push and clammer to get theirs first, using elbows and feet to good, if unladylike, effect. Moira is unmoved by all this racket. 'Just take your time, you'll all get your fags,' she shouts above the row. Another scrum at the filing cabinet behind her is hauling out handbags from where they are kept in the bottom drawer.

'You should see them in the office, it's bloody bedlam!' I tell

Rose, going into the kitchen. 'That's nothing,' Rose tells me. 'I was once on a male long-stay ward where the night staff forgot to leave the keys for the cigarette cupboard. The patients went mad when they couldn't have their fags, chasing us round the ward and shouting at the tops of their voices. Then one of them cracked the lass in charge across the head and we had to dive into the office and lock the door to get away from them. All you could see were these screaming faces at the window, all hammering to get in and shouting like maniacs. We had to phone the disturbed ward to send some male nurses down before we dare go out of the office. It was terrible. I think some of them would kill you for a fag, you know.'

I go upstairs and Betty comes towards me, another stark-naked female, or almost. She has her bra on but can't do it up at the back. It doesn't take a minute to snap the fasteners, then, remembering Moira's example, I warm my hands and push her breasts into the cups. Flop. They drop out again. I blow my hands and try again. Flop. Out they fall again. Betty doesn't speak, she's very passive and watches complacently as I try again to get her tucked away. Flop. Plop. Out they drop. In the end I go and get Tracy. 'For Christ's sake, Tracy, come and give me a hand with this,' I beg, mentioning the birthday boy. 'What's up?' she asks, raising an eyebrow questioningly. 'You'll see,' I tell her, getting hold of her arm. 'Come on.' She follows me down the ward as if I'm about to play a practical joke on her. Betty hasn't moved from her bedside. 'I can't get her fitted into that bra,' I explain rather sheepishly. 'They keep falling out.'

Tracy moves forward to examine the problem, though I'm pretty confident it's insoluble. 'Ha ha ha ha . . . Ha ha ha ha!' Tracy is staggering about the room laughing like a hyena. 'Well?' I demand. It takes a few minutes until she can speak. 'It's . . . it's . . . Ha ha . . . It's on upside down!' Again the silly bitch rolls off laughing and hooting. 'No wonder . . . Ha ha ha . . . no wonder they kept falling out!' So of course then the other two have to be told. Three women chortling away at me every time I run into them. Even Maisie appears, having popped in on the scrounge, bouncing her tits around and shouting, 'I hope these dinnae fall out, Buster.' Ha bloody ha!

By each bed is a pillowcase full of presents. Large pieces of card bearing the owner's name are attached with safety pins. Mostly it's cheap toiletries and a few fags and sweets with the odd present from relatives added. Here and there presents from the ladies to their friends on the ward. Most of the pillowcases are at least half full, some are overflowing. They are also largely undisturbed, attacked only with indifference. Sheila comes in; at 40 she is one of our younger patients. 'Do you like my new dress?' she says, not remembering my name and only knowing the dress is new because it still has a label on it. 'It's lovely, Sheila,' I reply, 'but come here and let me do the zip up and take that label off.' Obediently she stands still while I fasten her up. 'What did you get for Christmas, Sheila?' I ask. She looks at me incredulously; 'It's not Christmas, is it?' She has no memory for new events. 'Of course it is, Sheila. If you go to your room you'll find a pillowcase full of presents in it.'

She goes away and comes back empty-handed. She's crying, great blobbery tears running down her fat face. It's nearly more than she can stand. 'Which is my room?' she wails. 'I don't know which one it is.' We have a hug and then go up to her room together. She opens her presents and is delighted. We put them on her locker except the three she wants to keep with her, one of which is fags. 'What did Santa bring you then, Sheila?' Tracy asks when we return. Sheila shows her the things she's brought with her. 'What else did he bring you?' Tracy asks, knowing there is more. Sheila can't remember. Tracy can't believe it.

Tracy gets Martha to open her presents. Some of them are from abroad and well wrapped up. She looks through them and removes a large box of chocolates. When we turn round from making a bed she's gone, the presents lying where we left them.

Josie opens hers to see if there's any fags in them and to please us. She's totally uninterested in anything that isn't fags or money to buy fags. Standing there, a new compact in her hand that Moira went specially looking for in her own time, to replace Josie's old one, she says, 'Can I have a fag now?' No 'please' or

158

'thank you' or 'isn't it nice?'. I should be inured to this lack of response by now but it's still difficult for me to comprehend. Tracy's young girl's dream of Christmas in hospital is already shattered.

It's hard to believe the months of hard work that will have gone into this day. All those shopping trips up town to buy the patients presents from the staff; furtively hiding any presents that have come in from outside so that they last until the big day; taking the patients into town to make sure they all have at least one decent outfit for Christmas, then hiding it so that they don't spoil it before the big day. Moira will have spent the last three months budgeting for all these events; arranging transport for visits home; carefully stashing away some extra money from ward funds to buy a few drinks and delicacies; getting staff to agree what hours they're working and putting up with a lot of long faces from those who didn't get what they wanted; ordering stores and medicines and laundry to last over the holiday period; getting the ward decorated so that for a few days at least it looks half seasonal; making sure everybody has been to the hairdresser the week before and had a bath in the last two days. And all this activity depending so much on the good will of the nurses, who come in on afternoons off to take patients shopping and get nothing for it but their time back, and that only if they are lucky. They boost the miserly decorations, mostly last year's, with their own offerings given gratis, and shop for others while shopping for themselves, carrying twice as much home as they can manage without ever thinking it an imposition.

The dormitory is soon knee-deep in wrapping paper as Moira and Tracy keep bringing reluctant patients back upstairs to open their presents. Sophie totally refuses. We couldn't find her pillowcase first thing and by the time we did it was too late. Martha reappears from the toilets where she's been making a start on her chocolates. 'Oh, the men in my room last night,' she says. 'The dirty devils never gave me a minute's peace.' I don't agree with her, neither do I reinforce this recurring delusion. Her face is gypsy brown, the skin rendered photo-sensitive from years of being medicated with the tranquillizing Largactil. Josie has moved all the beds out of line and left them crooked, as she does every morning of the year. We straighten them back up again, as the staff do every morning of the year. 'It's a thin line!' I think to myself, not for the first time.

Eventually upstairs is sorted out and we go down. The ladies are eating their breakfast in ones and twos, just as they feel like it, instead of the usual rush. Except that they do still rush, even when there's no need. One can't just wave a magic wand one day of the year and expect everything to change because it's Christmas. There is a table set for our breakfasts which the ward maid has prepared. Nobody is in uniform. Mufti is a Christmas tradition here, showing how strong is the need for uniforms during the rest of the year. There is some muttering of discontent around the table as we await Moira. 'I hope we're going to have a drink soon,' Rose says. 'I mean, we've all put in. They all get a drink when they come through the door at seven o'clock on Jack Hurst's ward,' she tells me. I know what she's on about. Nobody really wants to start boozing at half past nine in the morning, or seven o'clock come to that, but when there's ten pounds of your money tied up in alcohol you at least want a chance to get some of it back before the afternoon staff guzzle the lot! 'She doesn't drink,' Tracy says. 'That's why she won't even think about us having one.' 'Just because she doesn't drink is no reason for us to go without,' Rose moans. 'I shall be having mine, I can tell you!'

The ward is well decorated. The vast ceilings brought down to a reasonable height for once in the year by the trailing streamers between the lights. The patients take little part in this activity, not being asked to help and even being put off when they do offer. Always the same excuses from the staff. 'She can't do it right.' 'You can't let them climb steps.' 'They'll mess it all up.'

'As you sow, so shall you reap.' Our harvest is apathy. Why should the patients get excited? It's our Christmas! The staff have organized it, chased around making all the arrangements, taken all the decisions. What is there in it for the patients? In front of me they eat at their various tables. Some eat quickly, gulping down their food. One patient licks her plate. Sophie starts to clear the crockery off her table before the others have finished and Moira has to tell her to leave it to avert trouble. Sophie is in a huff, wandering around saying what a terrible life it is and not doing much to improve matters. Her long-time girlfriend died last week and she doesn't know how to deal with the emotions that she's feeling but can't express. Of course our losing her pillowcase full of presents this morning hasn't helped matters. It's terrible to see her so unhappy, today of all days.

We have a good breakfast and take our time. There's nothing much we have to do today, no baths or hair-dos, no therapy or clinics. It's a holiday and the patients can do more or less what they like. In the day room behind me there is no interaction between the patients at all, some have already gone back to sleep, others sit there hallucinating freely. Carols blast forth from the telly but nobody is watching it. One middle-aged lady stands, her pinnie crumpled around her neck, rubbing her chin with a violent repetitive action. Another comes to the table at which we are eating, her face creased into a seemingly permanent expression of misery. 'I've wet myself,' she says, 'What'll I do? I've wet myself.' 'Go and get yourself changed,' Moira tells her kindly. 'Then put your wet clothes in to soak.' She doesn't move for a long time. Standing there with her miserable face, waiting for us to sort things out for her, ruining breakfast with her pissy smell. In the end she takes on the responsibility herself and goes off to change. A small victory?

Usually we dish out medications straight after breakfast. Today, because there is alcohol about, we omit all but essential drugs to try to avoid dangerous interactions. The patients are confused by this aberration from routine. They keep coming and asking when they will get their tablets.

Many of them have received gifts of cigarettes and are chain-smoking them, as if desperate to use up this usually scarce commodity and restore some balance to their black-market economy. Martha, who doesn't smoke, has already eaten one box of chocolates and is starting on another she has conned off Betty. She refuses to leave the ward, wouldn't even go to her sister's funeral, just stays here getting fatter and fatter despite all the diets invented for her. We sit and discuss presents received, past Christmases, which were always better than today's, what's on telly. Moira tries to turn the conversation to work. The rest divert it back to trivia.

'Well . . .' says Rose, getting to her feet. She has the dishes to do. We all dive in to help her, having little we want to do ourselves. 'Any sign of that drink yet?' Rose jokes to me as we dry up. Moira comes in on cue with some big bottles of lager and asks me to make up some shandy for the patients to drink. I put three jugs on a trolley and one-third fill them with lager, topping them up with lemonade. Rose has also gone into action. A glass of lager is pushed into my hands. 'We'll get a drink somehow,' she laughs as we knock the lager back in the kitchen, out of sight. The patients like the shandy and finish it in minutes. 'When are we having a cup of tea?' Martha asks, the shandy glass still in her hand, the chocolates on her lap.

Moira leads us in amongst them. Left to our own devices now we would be into the office and opening up the drink. 'What did Santa Claus bring you then?' Moira asks Sheila. They discuss the various items Sheila has in the pillowcase beside her chair, where she can be reminded of their existence. Moira is saying all the appropriate things but for some reason I'm finding it rather sickening today, almost condescending. I go over and sit by Betty, who has had no further escapes from her bra, because she will be happy just to show me her presents and doesn't require one of these inane conversations. She gets her presents out, one at a time, and gives them to me. We both look at them and handle them and smile a lot at each other. From the battered handbag which contains all her life she takes out a grubby handkerchief. In it is wrapped a small bundle of coins. She gives them to me, then, a few minutes later, takes them back again.

The schoolchildren are from nearby Hazel Leys. Schoolchildren, ha! They look more like the hordes of Genghis Khan. A new idea this, for them to come and sing carols. They find it hard not to laugh as they file into the middle of the day room. Hard not to laugh at all these old women sitting with their legs apart, picking their noses or smiling datelessly about them, calling out unexpectedly to them as Anthea now does, 'I'll clap you in irons, you bunch of cunts.' Anthea isn't even a patient on this ward but just visiting! She gets up and walks past me on her way out of the door, then comes back and stops in front of me, where I'm sitting on the right arm of Betty's chair. 'I've got a pad on!' she informs me.

The carol-singing starts ragged due to an outbreak of serious giggling as Anthea hitches up her dress and stands scratching her bum in the doorway. Soon, though, the kids get a grip on themselves and their voices ring out sweet and sharp.

> 'Away in a manger, no crib for a bed,
> The little Lord Jesus lay down his sweet head.'

Bloody hell, but these kids can't half sing. It's all good stuff and the ladies start to join in. Half of them only vaguely remember the words and keep diving in and out of the tune, which all adds to the poignancy of the scene as the choir look unbelievingly about them. Sheila sings suddenly, with a voice like an angel. She's got lungs like a coke-oven floor, a throat reminiscent of the fast lane of the M1, yet there she is soaring and swirling with the music. My eyes fill ridiculously with tears. This is too much to handle. I turn and pretend to talk to Betty and some of my tears fall on to her hands, clasped across her handbag. She looks at them and then slowly up at me.

We give the kids a cup of tea. They look askance at the monster pots we use as normal here. Some of the girls chat to the patients but the boys seem unable to. I talk to two of the girls and it's a minute before I twig that they're chatting me up. When they've gone the flak comes my way. 'I didn't think cradle-snatching was in your line,' Tracy joshes me. 'Buster, and you said you preferred older women,' Rose jokes. 'I bet all the girls chase you,' Martha says, trying to grab at my crotch with her free hand. The others are laughing again at my discomfiture. People that look like your granny shouldn't behave like this!

Time for another drink for the patients. This time it's sherry but still it has to be watered down with lemonade and served in the large glass jugs. It goes down well and we distribute some of the crisps and nuts. 'No, I can't eat nuts love, they get under my plate,' says Martha, pulling her top, chocolate-covered set of teeth out to illustrate the point.

Sheila has a coughing fit, induced by the nuts, which spray across the room like gunfire. She goes bluey-red in the face and starts hawking discoloured sputum up in long sticky streams that fall down across her party dress. It crosses my mind that she's going to die on me and for some ridiculous reason I get her to her feet and walk her through to the clinical room. Her emotional state is turning a coughing fit into something more dangerous, but it takes Moira to suss this out and calm her down, which cures the coughing. We go over the incident afterwards and I learn from the experience. 'Fancy doing any teaching on Christmas Day,' Rose says in disgust. Sheila has forgotten the whole incident by the time we get back to the day room and asks for a fag. When I refuse she howls, 'I want my family! Why can't I have my family?' She's a huge quivering mass of misery. We go into a hug and she clamps me to her. Eventually she calms down again.

Two nurses off another ward come on 'walkabout'. They can't believe we haven't got the drink out yet. 'I'm half pissed already,' one of them giggles. Rose comes back from next door, obviously with a few drinks inside her now. 'They want you,' she tells me, winking. But I know who's in charge today and the price of his company is too high, thinking what Maisie said he'd done to the patients and knowing what was happening to her. Instead my path goes across to the remembered smile of Zoe, who gives me a long, succulent, sherry-tasting kiss under the mistletoe. Mr Brown is on the settee asleep. Drunk yesterday, he's slept there all night rather than going home. He's not on duty until this afternoon. The patients come and look at him, go and sit down, then come and look at him again. As if they can't believe it, the hard life he leads them.

Ward to ward. In search of a little bit of Christmas spirit. Everywhere there's booze. I'm leaning on a radiator in the corridor talking to Rosemary when Mr Neale, his breath smelling of drink, turns aside momentarily and tells me off for slouching. We're the only nurses out on the ward, the rest are drinking in a side room. He's going to join them.

Rosemary goes on with what she was telling me. 'Can you imagine what it felt like when I found out it's one of my best mates who's been nicking all the stuff. And she's been using my name on all her forgeries. No wonder they kept questioning me. I thought it was just because I was black. How could she do that to me, the little bitch?' I listen for a while, letting her get it off her chest. I'm pleased it's all sorted out. 'Don't forget lunchtime in the club,' I remind her. 'I won't forget,' Rosemary laughs, her mood much improved. 'I'm getting hungry already!'

Another ward. Like Santa's Grotto. I have to duck to avoid the decorations groaning from the ceiling. On the walls of yet another ward, the twelve days of Christmas with only six painted in. At least its unfinished amateurishness shows the patients have been involved. 'There's nothing like spending Christmas in the bosom of one's family to send the average person daft, never mind this lot,' says Gloria, on Acutes. She adds, 'I don't think I've talked to a patient yet today.' 'I don't think I've seen one,' Sam quips, only half joking.

'Mabel went out on special leave last night,' Nikki tells me – adding, 'I hope she doesn't do anything silly.' 'Anything silly' in this case means things like turning on the car engine and shutting the garage door, like swallowing a fistful of tablets, like drawing a cool, clean blade across one's hot, bothered wrists. 'If she feels like killing herself all the time perhaps she's better off dead,' comments Gloria. Sam adds. 'I hope she does top herself, miserable bitch.' It makes me wonder why they bother to do the job and who took them on in the first place.

All around the hospital it's the same. There's something very sad about it all: the little rooms full of staff with the tables set out, laden with drink; the big rooms full of patients listening to carols on the telly; the odd early visitor traipsing through Acutes, not yet having learnt it's hopeless to hope; 70-per-cent proof kisses all tasting of fag smoke. And here a nurse drunk. I help the guy who's been groping her get her back to the ward she's come from. They send her home by taxi. I'm feeling bleak after all this and head back to my own ward.

'Buster, come and have a drink, bucko.' This from Micky, who looks like he's already had a few himself. We go upstairs to the disturbed ward. The first person I see is George, the top half of him that is, as he's standing the other side of a bed down in the dormitory with Luke and Dan. 'I thought he was working downstairs,' I say to Micky. 'What's he doing up here?' I guess I must have had a couple of drinks too. 'Ah, George,' says Micky, wiping some froth from his top lip before handing me a glass of ale. Then I see. George is wearing pyjamas. 'Oh no, I don't believe it,' I say. It feels like getting kicked in the stomach. But I do. I'd seen it in his eyes that day at the club. I'd known it then. 'He went bananas this morning, bucko,' Micky tells me quietly. 'On the ward. He was jumping off the beds, trying to fly and shouting that he was the King of the Angels.' For a moment even he's subdued, sipping his drink. 'Still, what the fuck!' he suddenly exclaims. 'We can always use an extra Messiah at this time of the year. That makes three at the last count!'

Christmas still has some magic. When I get back to the ward it's full of relatives visiting. We hardly ever get visitors here. There are people we've never seen before, who we didn't know existed. Others we see once or twice a year. Two we see frequently. I get the PR job and circulate round finding out who everybody is, making a note of their names and addresses, making pots of tea or dishing out something stronger. Anything to make them feel welcome so that they might come again. If only they knew how much we need their support. 'There's going to be some interesting blood-sugar readings tonight,' Moira says, watching the relatives of one of our diabetics stuffing her with chocolates.

At last we get our own drinks out. 'What'll you have, darling?' Rose asks coquettishly. 'Besides me, that is!' She's a scream with a few drinks inside her and I certainly need something to take me out of myself at the moment. We sit down in the office and drink and chat. 'I can't wait to get home and open my prezzies,' Tracy says. 'He'd better have got me that coat I hinted after,' Rose is telling Moira, 'or he'll be in the spare room tonight.' 'It's the kid's stuff that takes all the money – £20 for one of those little lorries our Julie paid.' This from a visitor off another ward. It rumbles on as we drink and eat the crisps and chocolates. Other staff pop in, have a drink and a kiss and depart again. Martha comes in. 'Hello dears,' she says. Her hand is already in the chocolate jar and five of them are lifted to her mouth in one huge gouge, rather like a dragline. 'Martha! Look at the mess you're making,' Rose reprimands her, getting a tissue and wiping her face. Martha hugs her. 'Santa Claus brought you something nice,' she squeals in Rose's face, 'down the chimney.' 'I'll give you down the bloody chimney,' Rose laughs.

'Can you come, Sister? Josie's fallen.' In the day room, where we all arrive together, Josie lies huddled at the foot of the radiator. There is a large cut across the bridge of her nose and she is unconscious. It sounds dramatic, but Josie, a chronic epileptic, falls like that at least once a week, crashing down wherever she happens to be. More than once she's fallen the length of the stairs. 'It's all those cigarettes she's been smoking,' Moira hypothesizes. 'They always set her off if she has too many.' We put her in a reclining chair handy to where she fell. There doesn't appear to be anything broken but I go and phone the doctor to come and check her over.

'Oh my bloody head,' Josie groans when she comes round, trying to lift her hand to it. Tracy brings in a wheelchair and we take her through to the clinical room. The Christmas outfit has blood on it now.

I sit and keep an eye on Josie, wondering what it would be like to live in a world where any second you could be plunged headlong into unconsciousness. The Doc says she's OK, but one can't just leave her alone to recover. Rose brings in another, younger, ward maid. Rose is wearing the skull cap Josie is supposed to keep on for her protection but doesn't because it's too hideous to look at. 'Here he is,' Rose says. 'Isn't he beautiful?' She stares into my eyes; there's laughter in hers. 'Anyway, enough of this adoration,' she giggles, breaking away. 'You're supposed to be a nurse; fix this young lass's hand up.' It's a sprain of the wrist and she's also hurt the back of her hand. I start bandaging. Rose stays to slag me off and clowns about in the skull cap, making Josie laugh so that her teeth pop out of her mouth and clatter on to the floor.

In the small alcove Moira has got half a dozen ladies singing carols with her. In the large day room a service booms out from the TV. I'm caught between the two waves of sound, which buffet me with childhood memories; to escape, I start to prepare for lunch. Christmas dinner, even here, is a special event and we try to make it something different. I push the individual tables together to make a big U-shaped communal table. There are sheets for tablecloths and they don't look too bad covered with the paraphernalia of eating. We even have Christmas napkins with holly in the corner and there are crackers to pull. It seems a pity nobody bothers to say Grace.

The first course is soup – there are no rolls, of course – followed by turkey or roast pork. The plates are scalding hot and we have to hand out a warning with each one. The wine, like the lager and the sherry, has been watered down with lemonade to make it stretch. I don't bother tasting it. We too sit down with the patients to eat, another break from the norm, dotting ourselves about and trying to stimulate conversation, or at least ensure everybody pulls a cracker and gets a party hat. I'm aware that yet again we are imposing our ideas of Christmas upon them. The food is surprisingly good, considering it's been made for hours, but the gravy has dried hard around the edges of the plates.

Moira proposes a toast. 'Merry Christmas Everyone,' she says, raising her glass. The response is ragged. The pace of the lunch is deliberately slow. We're trying to get them to savour the moment as something different. The ladies look around wondering what's holding up the next course, getting impatient with any break in routine. Our dinner is interspersed with serving theirs. Dishing out the Xmas pudding, rich and dark under its white sauce. Some of the ladies wolf it down and immediately get up and leave the table. 'What's the rush?' Tracy asks one of them, who pays her no attention. I can see she's miffed at all the hard work for no gratitude or appreciation. Betty smiles at me with her party hat on. The hats and crackers are the only festive touches to the meal. Conversation is noticeable by its absence, forced along by the nurses but always failing. It's all rather crushing.

There's no Report today, just a few drinks, and the morning staff can go home early. As we sit round the office I can see by the way the afternoon staff are attacking the drink that there isn't going to be any left tomorrow. At least they're going to enjoy themselves.

Suddenly Rose is there shouting, 'Sophie's upstairs on her bed with a plastic bag over her head.' For a second there's stunned silence. Tracy goes pale. It's as if we're in a little bubble of shock, everyone fearing the worst.

The afternoon staff nurse goes rushing off upstairs. I follow. For a change we're in time. My heart is pounding with the adrenalin. Sophie is standing by her locker, apparently having given up her suicide attempt at the arrival of Rose. 'You must take me for a real clown,' the staff nurse is saying, giving her a hard time. 'Now come on, where's the bag?' He searches her locker and finds it in a handbag on the top shelf. Sophie is twisting her hands anxiously. 'I'm sorry,' she says, 'I'm sorry.' It's not clear how she means that. She folds on to her bed and starts weeping. 'It's no good crying, Sophie, you shouldn't have done it in the first place,' he snaps, the adrenalin still pumping through his veins. It seems as if he's sorry there's nobody to resuscitate or lay out.

We discuss the incident after recharging our glasses. 'My God, I nearly fainted,' Tracy says, looking excited. 'I see you took your time getting there,' the staff nurse says to me, posturing to the girls as he does so. 'That's all we would have needed,' says Rose. 'I nearly died of shock when I saw her lying there.' 'I wonder why she decided to do it?' asks Moira. I tell nobody that I sent her up there to relax because she was looking a bit tense.

In the Social Club I find them playing bingo. It's hard to credit – eyes down, quiet as church mice – that this is Christmas Day. A crowd of us at the bar are spoiling their fun, whoever they are:

hardly any of these people sitting around the club work at the hospital. They are just mates and cronies of the committee, in for the free Christmas spread. 'I can drown you all out if I want to,' the clown calling out the bingo numbers threatens us. We take no notice. It's our club too. Our bloody Christmas. We're the ones who have been up since 5.30 this morning, so bollocks to you and your poxy bingo!

'Why don't you lot shut your row, you noisy bastards!' That's Mr Knowles speaking to us: Charge Nurse Knowles, a member of the committee, pissed, as he is in here every lunchtime of the year, work or no work. 'And why don't you go and fuck yourself?' This from another charge nurse, one of our crowd. He's a big lad and takes the wind out of Mr Knowles's sails. All we're doing is talking.

The stories start rolling out as the booze flows in. 'I'm telling you, man, she was in my class. She stood up in the middle of the lesson and said to the tutor, "Just because you're fucking me doesn't give you the right to ask me all these bloody questions." He didn't know where to put himself, silly twat.' Gales of laughter, clink of glasses. 'Aye and what about that time she lay down on the floor to demonstrate how he'd back-ended her the night before.' 'Serves him right, big-headed git.' 'That's what you get for shitting on your own doorstep.' 'And he said, "I don't want you to get too serious about me because the only thing I care for is my pigeons."' 'Ha ha ha!'

The theme switches to the old-timers, many of whom can still be seen around the club on days like these. Another pint is put in my hand. 'Honest to God, he stood right there and pissed against the bar, and never even bothered, just kept on drinking!' 'I can believe that, some visitors came on our ward one day and he was giving them the spiel when suddenly he stops, turns, gobs out of the window, then carries on.' A voice from the back of all the laughter shouts, 'What about that fat get, then, with the umbrella handle stuck up his arse!' We all know the story and are laughing at just the reminder of it. The jollity and sheer irreverence touch me for the first time that day with the festive feel of a holiday. Christmas, despite all the effort and good will, has only served to illustrate for me the yawning gap between this world in here and that one out there.

Joanna and Rosemary come in, as arranged, to go for Christmas dinner. Maisie has got a Christmas pudding, which looks like it's been nicked from the hospital kitchen; Rosemary and Joanna have made a lavishly decorated trifle. We go in a taxi, Rosemary and Maisie engaged in another of their usual good-natured arguments. Maisie's got blood on her hair, which is brushed over the bald patch pulled out this morning by an irate patient. Her eye is already going black. 'I don't care if they did let it happen,' Maisie's saying. 'I just want to be a good nurse, I'm not bothered about anything else.'

When we get to my house all the decorations on the trifle have sunk without trace.

Friday 26 July

On the last Friday in July, at the end of my last shift, I go into the laundry and hand in my white coats. There are eight of them altogether and one has a large rip down the back. 'You're leaving us then, Buster,' the seamstress says with a smile. She's the lady who kitted me out with these same uniforms nearly four years ago. 'Can't say I blame you,' she continues, checking my coats and writing the number in her little book. 'There's got to be better places than this to spend your life.'

Crossing over the open space in front of the hospital to await the bus into town, I feel at my back the brooding malignancy of this place resisting my departure, resisting all departures, as it has done now for nearly 150 years. I start to walk as if through treacle, my progress slowing as the institution seems to pull me back into its embrace, the bus stop taking on a mirage-like quality in the afternoon heat. Sweat runs down my face and wets the shirt on my back. On the bench, at the bus stop, an obese man lies smoking a matchstick-sized roll-up. As I slowly approach him he chuckles quietly to himself and it seems that nothing ever really changes in this place.

A light breeze springs up, refreshing me and wafting away the pungent smell of dried-on urine from the prone figure lying next to me. The institution and I survey one another across the open space between us. I try one last time to fathom out the mystery of its survival, searching for clues at the myriad windows, behind which all is hidden. But nothing is revealed. Sam the staff nurse emerges from the main entrance and swaggers across to come and sit down next to me. 'Shift over, Porky,' he says to the obese man, who slowly sits up, gets to his feet and rolls away.

'It's incredible,' I say to Sam, shaking my head. 'What's incredible?' he asks. 'That fat get?' 'No, this place,' I say. 'How anybody could ever believe a place like this might help somebody with a so-called mental illness is beyond me.' 'Go on, man,' Sam says. 'You can tell it's your last day. There's nowt up with this spot. That's just sour grapes because you're leaving.' 'Nothing wrong with it?' I exclaim. 'Just look at it. What a totally depressing sight! It's nothing but a slum, a sprawling, decaying Victorian slum, dropped down out here in the middle of bloody nowhere.' Sam grunts and takes out his *Daily Mirror*.

An ambulance stops opposite us. The ambulanceman goes round the back of the vehicle, opens up the doors and lets the steps down. Rosemary emerges, dressed in mufti, followed by a patient with his suitcase. She looks around, sees me on the bench and waves across. I wave back. The man, momentarily free of her attentions, looks apprehensively about him at the hospital buildings. Fear suddenly flickers across his face like summer lightning against a darkening sky. Rosemary notices his distress and takes his arm to reassure him, before leading him off towards the entrance. Already he is cowering, shoulders stooped, over-powered by the buildings that loom ominously above him.

'Look at that poor sod,' I say to Sam. 'I wonder how he'll get on in here? A short stay and a cure? Ha! On the roundabout perhaps? One of the 80 admissions out of every 100 who become re-admissions? Perhaps he's a chronic long-stay patient in the making? Ready for Rehabilitation in 30 years' time! Who knows, one day they might even put him in a chair and push him off down to Geriatrics.' 'What the fuck are you rabbiting on about?' Sam says, looking up from the bare-breasted girl on the page in front of him, then across to where Rosemary and her patient are about to be swallowed up by the hospital. 'You've got to put these nutters somewhere, you know. You can't just let 'em wander round the streets. I saw one tossing himself off in Marks and Sparks the other day. You can't have that sort of carry-on! They need to be looked after. He'll be all right in here, three cooked meals a day and no bills to pay, what more do you want?' 'There's more to life than three cooked meals a day,' I retort, a bit more sharply than I meant to, which obviously nettles Sam. 'Not if you're fucking starving there isn't,' Sam taunts me. 'Which is what you'll be doing soon, mate, packing up a good job in here.'

Across the way Rosemary applies some gentle pressure to ease her patient through the entrance, at which he has hesitated. 'I wonder how long it will take him to suss this joint out?' I say to Sam. 'To find out he's just become a nobody, that this place now has total control over his life?' 'You're on your high horse today, aren't you?' Sam criticizes. 'He wouldn't be in here unless he needed to be; this place is for the mentally ill, you know!' 'And what's mental illness then?' I challenge him. 'How can your mind be sick when nobody knows whether the mind even exists. Crazy is only what the psychiatrists say is crazy – there's no scientific test to say definitely if somebody is schizophrenic or manic or whatever – yet on one person's say-so we stick people in dumps like this, sometimes for the rest of their lives.' 'Get off with you, he'll probably be home in a couple of months,' says Sam. 'Anyway, it's not that bad in here if he has to stay, he can play bingo of a night, have trips out to the seaside, perhaps go to a holiday camp once a year. He'll soon pick up the routine. I don't know what you want, Buster, really I don't.' With a despairing shake of his head Sam returns to his *Daily Mirror*.

I sit and visualize Rosemary and her patient walking down the endless corridors. Already he will be finding out that the hospital is a dark, dirty and decaying labyrinth. Soon he will learn that privacy is a thing of the past, how it feels to wear another man's underpants, that the toilet doors don't lock, that except when required for some hospital ritual, or refusing to conform, he has become invisible. Walking down those corridors, does he realize that these walls around him are part of something that seems to have a life force of its own. As if it had not been built but rather planted here, growing unobserved in this isolated spot into its present monstrous form. That deep-rooted, hierarchical, authoritarian structure, carefully nurtured by generations of self-interest, prepared to stamp out ruthlessly any threat to its existence.

'This place has got a life of its own,' I say to Sam, drawing him reluctantly away from his paper once more. I guess I am a little high at the thought of finally leaving. 'It's this place that controls the staff, controls you, moulds people into what it wants. It strangles any initiative from day one; makes you dependent on a structure; rewards you for conforming to its wishes; keeps you in your custodial role by insisting doors are locked, using words like parole, holding people against their will. You're a prisoner of this place too, can't you see that? It's not only the patients who need to escape from here.' 'You, my friend,' says Sam, 'are full of shit. That's what's wrong with you. Strangling initiative! There's stacks of initiative. Look at that Jayne, you can't say she hasn't got plenty of get up and go. Her patients don't even have to get out of bed unless they want to. That's what I call initiative, leave the buggers in bed all day.' 'Jayne's ward was easily the best in the hospital,' I agree. 'But you're forgetting something. They shut it down, remember? Said it needed redecorating, then never opened it up again. Put her on a back ward away from the students and split up her ward team. As you say, mate, that's initiative!' Sam looks a bit put out at using such a bad example. 'That's just bad luck,' he argues. 'You're not trying to tell me they shut it down deliberately?' I smile grimly, remembering when I too would not have believed such a thing.

Sam changes tack. 'If you want to change things so much why don't you stay and help improve what's here? You can't deny things are better than they used to be.' 'They are,' I agree, 'but there have only been improvements in the way things are done, not in what we're actually doing. This place is still nothing more than a glorified lock-up, a chemical prison, and to me there's a basic conflict between therapy and custody which just can't be reconciled.' 'A basic conflict,' Sam sneers. 'You pompous arse, Buster.' I gesticulate at the buildings. 'Do you know that in 1962 the government said it would get rid of all the bins, yet today there's still nearly 65,000 people shut away in them.' 'What do you want to close these fuckers down for?' Sam asks sulkily. 'They're all right, they do a good job.' 'All right?' I snap, getting aerated. 'All right? You know putting patients in here means they end up having worse problems than they started out with. Would you nurse a bronchitic in a smoke-filled room? No, of course you wouldn't, so why are you doing what amounts to exactly the same thing to these people?'

I sit back and try to calm myself down – we're both getting a bit hot under the collar. 'We've always stuck people in the bin when they've played up a bit,' Sam says. 'You've got to stick them somewhere and it's better than locking them up in jail.' 'Is it?' I challenge him. 'At least if somebody goes to jail they have to go through the courts and when their sentence is up they get out. These poor sods don't get either of those luxuries. They get psychiatric labels stuck on them and then get locked away so that they won't disturb all the nice folks out there. Society, that's who controls the institution, controls the staff, controls the patient. They've made this place a dumping ground. Christ, 20,000 people a year are compulsorily admitted to hospitals just like this one, deprived of their liberty, treated without their consent. As long as society lets places like this exist, people will be incarcerated in them.'

'All right Mr Buster bloody know-it-all, where are you going to put all this crew if you don't keep them in here?' Sam asks. 'We need to keep people in the community,' I answer. 'Oh don't make me bloody laugh,' roars Sam. 'The community! That's the buggers that put 'em all in here in the first place!' 'Listen,' I snap. 'I said we need to keep people in the community. To stop admitting them into this place. If we don't separate people with problems from their family and friends then they have a chance to stay as part of their community.' 'Who's not listening to who?' Sam growls. 'I said where are you going to put all this crew if you don't keep them in here?' 'You're missing my point, Sam,' I respond. 'All you can think about is this place being closed down. That's the wrong way to approach it. The starting point should be how do we build up community services to prevent people coming in here, not how do we build up community services to accommodate people being discharged – that just leads to wrong thinking about the problem. It means you're trying to develop a psychiatric service out there to cater for a population in here

176

that's over 70-per-cent geriatric. That's nonsense. What's needed is to cut off the life blood of this place by stopping its supply of new patients. Do that and it won't take long to just wither away.'

'Excuse me,' Sam asks sarcastically, 'but didn't you say that as long as these places exist people will be admitted to them?' 'There is an alternative,' I respond. 'There's these new District General Hospital Psychiatric Units springing up everywhere. Now, OK, they're just big bins like this that have evolved into little bins, but it's part of the process. They give us the breathing space to develop community services properly on the one hand and run down the services in the bin on the other. They're a sort of half-way stage between the two but with the benefit of modern facilities.'

Sam looks sceptical. 'I think it's all a load of balls,' he says. 'What is the fucking community when it's at home, anyway? There's old patients of mine that live out there and they don't have half as good a time as they did in here. There's no social life; a lot of 'em are kicked out on to the street first thing in the morning and can't go home until late at night; some of 'em don't eat properly, and I know quite a few who don't even have a home to live in. Them that's gone back to their families are driving 'em nuts.' 'But that's exactly what happens when you're concentrating on closing down the bin rather than developing the community,' I argue. 'And do you think that anybody is going to spend the sort of money needed to set up a proper community service,' Sam asks derisively, 'when we can't even get the wards painted or keep them warm in winter? You're dreaming, Buster.' 'Maybe,' I say. 'But even you can't tell me there isn't a better way to look after people than this!' 'Bollocks,' snarls Sam, suddenly flaring up. 'This is the best place for 'em. Out of sight, out of mind. That's what your precious bloody public want. They won't thank you for dropping this fucking lot on their doorsteps. You're living in cloud-cuckoo-land, mate.'

The bus trundles into sight. Sam folds up his paper and gets to his feet. We stand, not talking, and when I take my seat Sam continues on up the aisle in a huff and sits by himself at the back of the bus. I slump sideways, tired of arguing, half leaning against the dirty, dusty windows. I'm not surprised at Sam's stance, which is a common one. His point of view would probably find sympathetic listeners in most of the mental hospitals in this country, where those with a vested interest in keeping the bins open wonder anxiously about their own futures.

To me, though, the only way forward is in the community. A chance to break the power of the bin. It's not enough to tinker, to put out a new syllabus like they did in 1982, the one I trained under, if you're going to leave the institution intact. Learners will still come out the same as Sam because institutional life attracts people like Sam. What's needed is people like Jayne – risk-takers, thinkers, individuals, people with character, people who can develop the new skills needed to work out there, in the community, where people live. And that's why the kind of nurse needed can never be produced in a bin like this, where the skills they need to learn are virtually non-existent. Anyway, the best education in the world would always be destroyed by the attitudes fostered and perpetuated within these walls. Attitudes that Sam shows in the extreme and with which all of us are tainted to some degree. And if we can't produce the quality of nurse we require, in the quantities needed to be effective, then who is ever going to help the poor bloody patients?

The bus slowly pulls away from the kerb. Beyond the dirty glass a distorted institution all too slowly passes into history. Despite myself I turn my head to catch at the last a vision of the disappearing towers.

FOR THE BEST IN PAPERBACKS, LOOK FOR THE (🐧)

In every corner of the world, on every subject under the sun, Penguin represents quality and variety – the very best in publishing today.

For complete information about books available from Penguin – including Pelicans, Puffins, Peregrines and Penguin Classics – and how to order them, write to us at the appropriate address below. Please note that for copyright reasons the selection of books varies from country to country.

In the United Kingdom: Please write to *Dept E.P., Penguin Books Ltd, Harmondsworth, Middlesex, UB7 0DA*

If you have any difficulty in obtaining a title, please send your order with the correct money, plus ten per cent for postage and packaging, to *PO Box No 11, West Drayton, Middlesex* .

In the United States: Please write to *Dept BA, Penguin, 299 Murray Hill Parkway, East Rutherford, New Jersey 07073*

In Canada: Please write to *Penguin Books Canada Ltd, 2801 John Street, Markham, Ontario L3R 1B4*

In Australia: Please write to the *Marketing Department, Penguin Books Australia Ltd, P.O. Box 257, Ringwood, Victoria 3134*

In New Zealand: Please write to the *Marketing Department, Penguin Books (NZ) Ltd, Private Bag, Takapuna, Auckland 9*

In India: Please write to *Penguin Overseas Ltd, 706 Eros Apartments, 56 Nehru Place, New Delhi, 110019*

In Holland: Please write to *Penguin Books Nederland B.V., Postbus 195, NL–1380AD Weesp, Netherlands*

In Germany: Please write to *Penguin Books Ltd, Friedrichstrasse 10–12, D–6000 Frankfurt Main 1, Federal Republic of Germany*

In Spain: Please write to *Longman Penguin España, Calle San Nicolas 15, E–28013 Madrid, Spain*

In France: Please write to *Penguin Books Ltd, 39 Rue de Montmorency, F-75003, Paris, France*

In Japan: Please write to *Longman Penguin Japan Co Ltd, Yamaguchi Building, 2–12–9 Kanda Jimbocho, Chiyoda-Ku, Tokyo 101, Japan*

FOR THE BEST IN PAPERBACKS, LOOK FOR THE 🐧

A SELECTION OF FICTION AND NON-FICTION

A Confederacy of Dunces   John Kennedy Toole

In this Pulitzer-Prize-winning novel, in the bulky figure of Ignatius J. Reilly, an immortal comic character is born. 'I succumbed, stunned and seduced . . . it is a masterwork of comedy' – *The New York Times*

The Labyrinth of Solitude   Octavio Paz

Nine remarkable essays by Mexico's finest living poet: 'A profound and original book . . . with Lowry's *Under the Volcano* and Eisenstein's *Que Viva Mexico!*, *The Labyrinth of Solitude* completes the trinity of masterworks about the spirit of modern Mexico' – *Sunday Times*

Falconer   John Cheever

Ezekiel Farragut, fratricide with a heroin habit, comes to Falconer Correctional Facility. His freedom is enclosed, his view curtailed by iron bars. But he is a man, none the less, and the vice, misery and degradation of prison change a man . . .

The Memory of War and Children in Exile: (Poems 1968–83)   James Fenton

'James Fenton is a poet I find myself again and again wanting to praise' – *Listener*. 'His assemblages bring with them tragedy, comedy, love of the world's variety, and the sadness of its moral blight' – *Observer*

The Bloody Chamber   Angela Carter

In tales that glitter and haunt – strange nuggets from a writer whose wayward pen spills forth stylish, erotic, nightmarish jewels of prose – the old fairy stories live and breathe again, subtly altered, subtly changed.

Cannibalism and the Common Law   A. W. Brian Simpson

In 1884 Tod Dudley and Edwin Stephens were sentenced to death for killing their shipmate in order to eat him. A. W. Brian Simpson unfolds the story of this macabre case in 'a marvellous rangy, atmospheric, complicated book . . . an irresistible blend of sensation and scholarship' – Jonathan Raban in the *Sunday Times*

FOR THE BEST IN PAPERBACKS, LOOK FOR THE

A CHOICE OF PENGUINS

The Diary of Virginia Woolf
Five volumes edited by Quentin Bell and Anne Olivier Bell

'As an account of intellectual and cultural life of our century, Virginia Woolf's diaries are invaluable; as the record of one bruised and unquiet mind, they are unique' – Peter Ackroyd in the *Sunday Times*

Voices of the Old Sea   Norman Lewis

'I will wager that *Voices of the Old Sea* will be a classic in the literature about Spain' – *Mail on Sunday* 'Limpidly and lovingly Norman Lewis has caught the helpless, unwitting, often foolish, but always hopeful village in its dying summers, and saved the tragedy with sublime comedy' – *Observer*

The First World War   A J P Taylor

In this superb illustrated history, A J P Taylor 'manages to say almost everything that is important for an understanding and, indeed, intellectual digestion of that vast event . . . A special text . . . a remarkable collection of photographs' – *Observer*

Ninety-Two Days   Evelyn Waugh

With characteristic honesty Evelyn Waugh here debunks the romantic notions attached to rough travelling; his journey in Guiana and Brazil is difficult, dangerous and extremely uncomfortable, and his account of it is witty and unquestionably compelling.

When the Mind Hears   Harlan Lane
A History of the Deaf

'Reads like a suspense novel . . . what emerges is evidence of a great wrong done to a minority group, the deaf' – *The New York Times Book Review* 'Impassioned, polemical, at times even virulent . . . (he shows) immense scholarship, powers of historical reconstruction, and deep empathy for the world of the deaf' – Oliver Sacks in *The New York Review of Books*

FOR THE BEST IN PAPERBACKS, LOOK FOR THE

A SELECTION OF FICTION AND NON-FICTION

Cat's Grin François Maspero

'Reflects in some measure the experience of every French person . . . evacuees, peasants, Resistance fighters, *collabos* . . . Maspero's painfully truthful book helps to ensure that it never seems commonplace' – *Literary Review*

The Moronic Inferno Martin Amis

'This is really good reading and sharp, crackling writing. Amis has a beguiling mixture of confidence and courtesy, and most of his literary judgements – often twinned with interviews – seem sturdy, even when caustic, without being bitchy for the hell of it' – *Guardian*

In Custody Anita Desai

Deven, a lecturer in a small town in Northern India, is resigned to a life of mediocrity and empty dreams. When asked to interview the greatest poet of Delhi, Deven discovers a new kind of dignity, both for himself and his dreams.

Parallel Lives Phyllis Rose

In this study of five famous Victorian marriages, including that of John Ruskin and Effie Gray, Phyllis Rose probes our inherited myths and assumptions to make us look again at what we expect from our marriages.

Lamb Bernard MacLaverty

In the Borstal run by Brother Benedict, boys are taught a little of God and a lot of fear. Michael Lamb, one of the brothers, runs away and takes a small boy with him. As the outside world closes in around them, Michael is forced to an uncompromising solution.

A CHOICE OF PENGUINS

Trail of Havoc Patrick Marnham

In this brilliant piece of detective work, Patrick Marnham has traced the steps of Lord Lucan from the fateful night of 7th November 1974 when he murdered his children's nanny and attempted to kill his ex-wife. As well as being a fascinating investigation, the book is also a brilliant portrayal of a privileged section of society living under great stress.

Light Years Gary Kinder

Eduard Meier, an uneducated Swiss farmer, claims since 1975 to have had over 100 UFO sightings and encounters with 'beamships' from the Pleiades. His evidence is such that even the most die-hard sceptics have been unable to explain away the phenomenon.

And the Band Played On Randy Shilts
Politics, people and the AIDS epidemic

Written after years of extensive research by the only American journalist to cover the epidemic full-time, the book is a masterpiece of reportage and a tragic record of mismanaged institutions and scientific vendettas, of sexual politics and personal suffering.

The Return of a Native Reporter Robert Chesshyre

Robert Chesshyre returned to Britain from the United States in 1985 where he had spent four years as the *Observer*'s correspondent. This is his devastating account of the country he came home to: intolerant, brutal, grasping and politically and economically divided. It is a nation, he asserts, struggling to find a role.

Women and Love Shere Hite

In this culmination of *The Hite Report* trilogy, 4,500 women provide an eloquent testimony of the disturbingly unsatisfying nature of their emotional relationships and point to what they see as the causes. *Women and Love* reveals a new cultural perspective in formation: as women change the emotional structure of their lives, they are defining a fundamental debate over the future of our society.